TREATMENT OF THE DELINQUENT ADOLESCENT

Group and Individual Therapy With Parent and Child

Harris B. Peck, M.D.

Director, Bureau of Mental Health Services,
New York City Court of Domestic Relations
Lecturer in Psychiatry, The New York School of Social Work,
Columbia University

and

Virginia Bellsmith

Professor and Assistant Dean,
The New York School of Social Work, Columbia University
Formerly, Chief Psychiatric Social Worker,
Treatment Service, Bureau of Mental Health Services,
New York City Court of Domestic Relations

FAMILY SERVICE ASSOCIATION OF AMERICA
192 Lexington Avenue   New York 16, N. Y.

Library of Congress Catalog Card Number: 54–9622

Printed in U. S. A.   Price, $2.00

CONTENTS

CONTENTS

PREFACE

This book is written out of the experience of the authors who, over a period of years, wrestled with the theoretical, technical, and administrative problems of providing treatment services in a children's court setting for delinquent adolescents and their parents. It offers some tentative solutions to the problems that make the going so rough in this field. It reflects some of the gains that have been made, in the application of psychiatric, psychological, and casework principles to these difficult problems of behavior, by the courts and allied services and institutions. An attempt is made to weigh achievements and potentialities against failures and limitations. This book does not undertake to cover all the possible approaches to the problem of delinquency. Rather, attention is focused on the methods and techniques that seem to have special significance in extramural treatment of delinquent adolescents and their families. A fairly detailed presentation is given those treatment practices and processes that seem especially useful in this type of work.

The materials in this volume could not have been assembled solely through the efforts of the authors. We are indebted to the administration of the New York City Court of Domestic Relations and especially to its Presiding Justice, John Warren Hill, for providing us with the opportunity to engage in the kind of practice and experimentation discussed in these pages. Many of the case illustrations have been drawn from the work of our colleagues in the Treatment Service of the Bureau of Mental Health Services; they also participated in the day-to-day process of hammering out and shaping the concepts that we are presenting. The support of the judges and probation officers has been an essential ingredient in the creation of a treatment program geared to the needs of children and their parents, within a court setting.

1

PREFACE

A special debt of gratitude is due Dr. Marion E. Kenworthy, Professor of Psychiatry, at the New York School of Social Work, Columbia University, who almost single-handedly enlisted the support of interested lay and professional people in the establishment of a treatment clinic at the court in 1937. Private foundation funds supported the program until 1946. The supervisor and student staff were recruited by the New York School of Social Work. The student program continues as part of the present Bureau of Mental Health Services which is now an integral part of the court structure. Credit should also be given to Dr. Helen Montague, director of the clinic from 1937–1953, and to Judge Justine Wise Polier, who have given creative leadership to the development of the treatment program.

No joint writing venture such as this, which has extended over a period of five years, would have been possible without the interest and assistance of our secretaries. Special thanks should go to Miss Agnes Foote for her extensive and valuable help.

Charlotte Peck and Henry Bellsmith, in spite of the inevitable suffering imposed on them as the wife and husband of the authors of this joint venture, made their own unique, creative contributions, for which we are both deeply grateful.

HARRIS B. PECK, M.D.
VIRGINIA BELLSMITH

INTRODUCTION ❋

Delinquents are troublesome! Youthful offenders are not only a source of annoyance and concern to their parents and teachers but, in addition, they present the community and its agencies with a number of seemingly insoluble problems. Enlightened public opinion has been forcing the abandonment of much of the old penal and custodial machinery for delinquent juveniles and is questioning its value even for adult offenders. Early in this century many communities, in attempting to develop courts, institutions, and treatment facilities that would be suitable for the needs of the delinquent, turned for help to the then budding professions of psychiatry, social work, and clinical psychology. Some of the first child guidance clinics were originally founded for the express purpose of providing services for juvenile courts. Most of the clinics, however, separated themselves from this alliance or, in other instances, were repudiated by the courts.

It is probably not valid to attribute the failure to consummate what was doubtless a premature marriage solely to the "inherent nature" of either the courts or the clinics. Courts and clinics have undergone many changes in the past quarter century and behavior is now better understood by both. There is less rigidity about the precise conditions under which it is considered permissible to carry on casework or therapy. In many fields there is a movement to re-evaluate critically some of the sacred "classical" approaches which have not been too successful with certain types of problems.

In retrospect it now seems clear that an unreasonable demand was placed on social workers in family agencies or child guidance clinics when they were expected, without benefit of special preparation, to work collaboratively with children's courts or directly with authoritative agencies dealing with delinquents. Also it is now recognized that psychiatrists require considerable training (and

3

some retraining) before they are able to move from private practice to functioning as useful members of an agency staff. Yet at that time there was the expectation that the practices of child guidance clinics or family agencies could be transferred in toto to a group of clients and to a setting that had certain familiar aspects but had also many unique characteristics.

Many of the young persons who pass through a children's court are, of course, little different from those who do not. But whether anxiety is manifested by enuresis or in stealing is not simply a fortuitous matter. Nor is it altogether accidental that a delinquent child appears in court. And once he has appeared in court, the total dynamic situation confronting him and his family undergoes considerable change. Professional persons who are going to work with delinquents and their parents might do well, as minimal preliminary preparation, to acquaint themselves with some of the special features of these clients as well as of the institutions and agencies that traditionally have handled them.

These institutions—the courts, the detention centers, the juvenile police, the training schools—also have a sizable task if they are to transform their archaic structures into effective scientific social instruments. Overburdened as they are, change in orientation will not, in itself, offer much relief. Adding clinical personnel to the payroll, or working out a co-operative arrangement with a community agency, will not melt away incredibly large case loads or provide magical solutions for the many technical and administrative problems facing the agency. The basic problems—the shortage of trained personnel and the lack of adequate community resources —must be attacked on the broad front of responsible community action. Without such action there is a tendency to try to utilize treatment services in ways which are inappropriate and which limit their unique potentials.

I. Patterns of Pathology

THE FACTORS THAT CONTRIBUTE to a type of behavior that society calls "delinquent" are in many ways similar to those that produce other types of human behavior. On the other hand, a wide variety of delinquent activities are characterized by a number of common elements and form a kind of symptom complex. Although the etiology of the symptom complex is not fully understood, the frequent presence of certain contributing agents in delinquent acts suggests that the etiology follows a general pattern.

Prior to the development of modern psychiatry, a chief criterion for identifying certain behavioral disorders was the degree to which the person afflicted was dangerous either to himself or to the community at large. Incarceration was then the remedy applied. Today these disorders would be classified, on the one hand, as psychotic disturbances and, on the other, as criminal or delinquent behavior. Originally the custodial care for both groups was the same and even today considerable confusion exists, both in identifying and in treating these two categories of ill persons.

A strong taint of moral judgment still remains in the public mind about mental illness and is reflected in the kind of minimal custodial care provided in many state hospitals. An even stronger attitude of moral disapprobation is directed toward the delinquent, as is evidenced by the periodic campaigns launched by the press for stringent control and wholesale institutionalization of adolescents whose behavior deviates from the presumed mores of the community. Unfortunately, such irrelevant moralizing tends to hinder the development of public understanding of both psychotic and delinquent behavior and thereby to postpone the establishment of services to meet their needs.

These negative attitudes of the community toward mental illness and delinquency are based, however, on a vague recognition of certain central elements in the pathology of both. The gross disintegration and defective reality contact of the psychotic motivate society to place him in an institution. In delinquency, custodial placement is often society's response, not only to the overt symptoms of a complex emotional illness which it intuitively recognizes, but also to the hostility that is a characteristic component of the pathology in the delinquent.

In the United States delinquents are generally handled by the police, the courts, social agencies, and specific custodial institutions. For the most part it is the nature of the community structure and the character of the act rather than the kind of disturbance in the individual who commits the act which determine the type of agency that will handle the case. Most authorities are in agreement that, in the light of present scientific knowledge, the category "delinquency" has only legal or moral meaning and is of little value in understanding pathology or in devising methods of treatment. A child who is adjudged delinquent in juvenile court may, upon psychiatric study, be shown to be manifesting in his act the symptoms of a process that may range anywhere from the most severe organic or psychotic illness to a transient reflection of an acute situational crisis.

The delinquent group includes adolescents whose disturbance may fall in any one of a variety of neurotic or psychotic illnesses, the so-called conduct disorders, or the controversial classification of the psychopathies. In addition, delinquent behavior may occur in adolescents with defective intelligence or it may have no essential connection with intellectual capacity. The disinclination on the part of some therapists and social workers to explore the relationship of symptoms to these various syndromes is perhaps

6

in part a result of the earlier mechanistic efforts to delimit *a psychopathology* of *the* delinquent. In this unilateral approach an attempt was made to discover a basic dynamism universally applicable to all delinquents. The contrasting multiple approach is perhaps a logical outcome of the relatively recent expansion of knowledge of individual psychology. Currently there is growing insistence on the need for differential diagnosis as the only scientific basis for treatment methods designed to meet diverse individual needs. Despite the enormous contribution of this latter approach, the emphasis on individual diagnosis has tended to obscure certain basic interrelationships that exist among the syndromes comprising the delinquencies that were intuitively, though incompletely, grasped by some of the earlier workers in the field.

Social Pathology and Hostility

If, on examination of a collection of processes labeled delinquent, certain common or unifying characteristics were found to be present, this knowledge might be integrated with the present understanding of pathology and etiology and form the base for beginning a scientific study of the epidemiology of delinquency. Such a study would seem to be essential to the development of a really sound mental hygiene approach to delinquency. Since epidemiologists are always alert to the geographic distribution of an illness, the characteristic patterns of high delinquency concentration within certain community areas would doubtless be a major point of study. Because the delinquent is characterized by the hostile impulses manifested in his symptoms, there is a temptation to make stereotyped assumptions about the causal connections between the social pathology of certain neighborhoods and the hostility evident in the behavior of delinquent individuals. Although it is true that individuals have sharply differing kinds of psychopathology, it is also true that certain common elements in the symptom of hostility itself exist and provide at least a partial explanation of the correlation between the incidence of delinquency and environmental conditions.

In a study of the genesis and nature of hostile behavior, Bender defines aggression as "a symptom complex resulting from depri-

7

vations which are caused by developmental discrepancies in the total personality structure such that the constructive patterned drives for action in the child find inadequate means of satisfaction and result in amplification or disorganization of the drives into hostile or destructive aggression." [1] She also points out that deprivation in the early years of life is perceived as such: "Since the child is under the impression, based upon experience, that the adult can satisfy these needs, he thus considers any deprivation of them as an act of aggression from the adult and reacts accordingly. The child acts as though there were an inherent awareness of his needs and there is thus the expectation of having them met. A failure in this regard is a deprivation and leads to frustration and a reactive aggressive response." [2]

If hostility, which is an inherent part of delinquent behavior, is hypothesized to be causally related to deprivation, a correlation between the particular character of the delinquency and both the qualitative nature and chronological occurrence of the deprivation may be assumed. A detailed clinical study and scrutiny of the histories of over a thousand cases at the clinic appear to bear out this formulation. When the delinquent acts for which children were brought into court were classified, they fell into three major categories: (1) acts against life and property (such acts frequently occur as part of gang activity which may not, however, constitute pathological behavior or even delinquency per se); (2) acts in violation of sexual taboos, or symbolic equivalent of such acts; (3) acts directed against the restraint or restrictions of parents or parental surrogates such as teachers, neighbors, or police.

In attempting to analyze the kind of major deprivations experienced by these children, we placed them in categories that correspond to the various childhood developmental phases.

First, as infants they experienced the deprivation of such love manifestations as handling, fondling, kissing, parental attention, as well as more specific basic biological lacks in food, warmth,

[1] Lauretta Bender, M.D., "Genesis of Hostility in Children," *American Journal of Psychiatry,* Vol. CV, No. 4 (1948), p. 242.
[2] *Ibid.*

and opportunity for motor activity. The absence of any of these essentials constitutes a defect in the basis for the infant's growth and security.

Second, during the period from 3 to 6 years of age, the child's deprivations stem from the inadequacies of the interpersonal relationships within the family constellation. During this phase of development, disturbances in the parental relationships, such as separation or infidelity of parents, may warp the emotional development of the child. Although the child during this period has attained the potential for independent motion and movement, he must still depend largely on adult consent and support for his actions; therefore, the parents' attitudes toward the child and his activities will critically affect his entire basic mode of operation.

Third, from the age of 6 on, the most significant deprivations for the child seem to be related to interference with his accelerated needs for social expression. His growth struggle at this period is to gain mastery of an enlarged environment and to develop physical, intellectual, artistic, and social skills.

In most of our clinic cases we found that neither the nature nor the intensity of reaction to these deprivations was extreme enough to bring the child into court much before adolescence, even though his history might reveal the existence of some symptoms at earlier periods. The relative helplessness of the younger child to carry even the most powerfully motivated rebellion far beyond the confines of the family, and the fact that children's courts are primarily designed to protect the community, doubtless account for the preponderance of adolescents in the cases brought to court. Very young children usually come under court jurisdiction only when the family structure is so completely disintegrated as to demand the intervention of the community. In such cases the petition on which the child is brought to court is often one of neglect rather than delinquency.

Although the severe delinquent reactions necessitating court action reach a peak in the pre-adolescent and adolescent years, even in cases of an acute explosive onset a careful history usually reveals earlier deprivational experiences during one of the critical developmental periods in the child's life. The factors that exert a decisive influence on the expression of delinquent or acting-out

9

behavior—rather than the manifestation of neurotic or internalized pathology—seem to be largly related to the adolescent's needs and frustration.

The relative frequency with which delinquent reactions are expressed during adolescence seems to indicate that their genesis is intimately interwoven with the developmental problems of the period itself. Adolescence is a critical and decisive phase in the individual's struggle to reach adulthood and master his world. The development of new physical strengths and of social skills, and the heightening of his strivings toward and against other people, set the stage for the actual life role that he will play. In many cultures it is the time at which society formally confers the prerogatives of manhood and womanhood upon the individual. Even in the complex culture of a country such as ours, a 13- or 14-year-old child may occasionally manage a more or less independent existence. An adolescent may marry with or without parental consent, may hold a responsible job, or, by lying about his age, may serve in the armed forces.

Usually, society demands that the adolescent's freedom be closely curbed and his independence exerted only in circumscribed areas allotted to him. His rewards for such conformity are often rather meager, frequently constituting only vague hopes that cannot be fulfilled for another five, ten, or even more years. Socially acceptable behavior by the adolescent requires a high degree of frustration tolerance. He is expected to accept and adjust to values which are not only insubstantial but which bear little relation to the powerful psychological and biological pressures he is trying to control. He can no longer function adequately by dependence on parental identification since normal development in adolescence is characterized by movement away from parents. And yet, as noted by Redl,[3] the adolescent's successful transition from a world peopled by parental figures to one of ideas and values depends on factors in the individual's past experiences as well as his present life situation. He is expected to operate on the basis of certain ethical systems and ideological considerations whether or not these have been explicitly verbalized into a specific moral code.

[3] Fritz Redl, "Pre-Adolescents—What Makes Them Tick?" *Child Study*, Vol. XXI, No. 2 (1944), p. 44.

This shift in adult perspective about adolescent behavior is particularly apparent in the court setting, and is manifest in the attitudes of parents, teachers, court officials, and society generally. Reactions and behavior tolerated in the child are held to be intolerable in the adolescent. Although it is true that the character of the adolescent's delinquent acts is different from the child's, it is also true that society has a different attitude about the adolescent's responsibility for his acts. The adolescent, who is struggling to master his environment, is likely to express his conflicts in areas beyond the confines of the family group. When the struggle ends in the courtroom, this result is not due solely to the character of the experiences within the family prior to adolescence. The opportunities for constructive and satisfying experiences made available to him by the community—in schools, recreational centers, clinics, vocational guidance services, and job possibilities—also play a large part in determining whether or not he reaches a court.

Quite often an adolescent who is not too seriously disturbed, but who can no longer conform to the demands made upon him by his family, will make a number of abortive attempts to achieve what for him may be positive and constructive goals, only to find that they eventually bring him into court. An adolescent, for instance, may flee from a school situation only after repeated demands have been made upon him in excess of his social, emotional, or intellectual capacities. While truanting he may attempt to get a job, again in violation of society's standards. The fact that he is finally driven to achieve what he wants in an irregular fashion is often the result of a series of factors that reinforce each other, including disturbed parental relationships, the unsatisfactory nature of extra-familial and neighborhood life, and the inadequate facilities within the community and its agencies for meeting his needs.

Since this kind of coincidence occurs most frequently within the most impoverished areas of the community, it would seem that the connection is not an accidental one. Rather, it suggests that a clear relationship exists between individual failures of adjustment and the defects in social arrangements that are so especially evident in deprived areas. It may be said that the

11

residents of these areas are discriminated against socially, and thus made vulnerable to the kind of pathology found in delinquency.

Diagnostic Categories

In making a distinction between the internalized type of neurotic pathology and the delinquent or acting-out type of reactions, we do not consider that such acting-out reactions of the delinquencies represent a diagnostic entity. The diagnostic categories in which our clinic patients fall include a wide variety of syndromes ranging from a few early or latent schizophrenics, a sprinkling of psychopaths, a number of adolescents in acute neurotic crises, and the mixed diagnostic syndromes so frequently seen in children. There is, however, a significant concentration of adolescents with severe conduct disorders [4] and long-standing, chronic, neurotic pathology manifested primarily in character disturbances. Patients in these last two groupings usually manifest behavior that appears psychopathic in character; they can be differentiated from the true psychopath on the basis of history, clinical observation, and psychological testing. At the clinic, relatively few children are classified as true psychopaths since this group is sharply delimited; we apply the criteria that have been delineated by such writers as Bender, Rabinovitch, Spitz, Goldfarb, and Karpman.[5] We refer, however, to certain severe conduct disorders and character neuroses—because of their apparent psychopathic nature—and to true psychopathy as *the psychopathies.*

[4] At our clinic the diagnosis of conduct disorder is applied most frequently to pre-adolescent children. Following puberty, children whose disturbances might previously have been diagnosed as conduct disorder tend to develop symptomatology that places them either in the category of neurotic or of character disorder. The criteria employed in the diagnosis of conduct disorder correspond more or less to those formulated by J.H.W. van Ophuijsen, M.D., of the Jewish Board of Guardians. See *Primary Behavior Disorder in Children,* by Staff Members, Jewish Board of Guardians. Family Service Association of America, New York, 1945.

[5] Much of the following material on psychopaths is derived from the formulations of these writers. See "The Psychopathic Delinquent Child: Round Table, 1949," *American Journal of Orthopsychiatry,* Vol. XX, No. 2 (1950), pp. 223–265.

A typical history of true, or extreme, psychopathy is manifest in a child who has had an almost complete lack of opportunity for a relationship with one or both parents, or parental figures, for a prolonged period before his fifth year, and particularly during his first two or three years of life. Classically, the syndrome is seen in children who spend a part of their infancy in the aseptic atmosphere of a certain (now disappearing) type of "orphanage." Frequent shifts in foster home placement may bring about a similar absence of opportunity for adequate parental relationships. These children in adolescence characteristically show an intolerance for even minor frustration and a strong need for immediate impulse gratification. Clinically, there seems to be an almost complete absence of guilt or anxiety, although severe temper tantrums are not uncommon.

Many of these adolescents appear superficially attractive, but even brief contact with them indicates that they are actually incapable of establishing meaningful relationships with others. They are difficult to educate; for many reasons, but especially because of their defective time perception, they do not seem to be able to profit from past experiences. If given psychometric tests over a period of years, they usually score low during the first few years of life, go up somewhat at about the fifth year or upon beginning school, but drop again as they continue in school and have difficulty in learning or, later, as they should be acquiring the social and verbal insights required of adolescents. In later adolescence, they are sometimes mistaken for manic-depressives because of their wide mood swings which seem to be almost in direct response to biologic rhythms. Despite, or perhaps because of, these handicaps they become adept at certain kinds of social maneuvering and unconflictedly employ lies and evasions to achieve immediate pleasure and impulse gratification and to avoid the consequence of their behavior.

Only in the true psychopath will all these symptoms be found. However, a significant number of these elements are generally present, to a varying degree, in all the adolescents in the diagnostic entities characterized as the psychopathies.

The psychopathies are also characterized by the acting out of conflict, usually in a hostile manner. Clinically, the difference

13

between the true psychopath and persons suffering from certain character neuroses and severe conduct disorders is chiefly in the degree of superego defect and of uninhibited impulse gratification, and in absence of guilt and anxiety. Writers in the field differ as to whether the apparent absence of guilt and anxiety represents their repression beyond the reach of clinical study and therapeutic endeavor or their incorporation into the distorted character structure in a form that renders them clinically different from the way they appear in other syndromes. Differences in the life experiences of the individuals, however, seem to influence significantly the final diagnostic picture. A differentiation between the true psychopathy and the other psychopathies can generally be made on the basis of the character of the parental relationships; actual absence of a relationship is more damaging than a relationship perceived by the child as a rejecting one. The age of onset of these defects in the parental relationship and their duration are of great importance. The extremes of psychopathy are most likely to appear in individuals for whom the relationship defect is most complete and prolonged before the age of 4 or 5.

Discrepancy Between Needs and Satisfactions

The age factor is probably only a specific outward sign of the various influences that affect the child in a certain phase of development. Growth curves, charting the individual's development in various areas of functioning such as the motor, sexual, educational, or social areas, show acceleration in particular developmental areas at particular periods of time in the child's life. It therefore seems probable that disturbances in particular areas of functioning of an individual are related to inadequacies in the physical and social environment of the child at the time of accelerated development in this area. Our experience at the clinic indicates that such coincidence exists between defects in character structure resulting in delinquency and defects in the environment at the early developmental period. The extent and the duration of the deprivation, at any age level, naturally will affect the degree of disturbance in a particular phase of growth. Obviously, the greater the actual number and frequency of all sorts of de-

14

priving experiences, the greater will be the likelihood of the kind of coincidences referred to above.

Physical limitations, both within the organism and in its environment, contribute to the incidence of this kind of developmental discrepancy. Organic defects, whether they be constitutional or a result of brain damage, increase the likelihood that the environment will not be able to fulfil the increased demands of the organism. Economic and cultural deprivation, in the same way, are significant conditioning factors since they tend to reduce the opportunities for compensatory and substitute gratifications. The initial frustrating experiences within the family, therefore, are more likely to be repeated in an inimical environment—at school, in the play or social groups, and ultimately with the police, judges, and probation officers. Each of these experiences tends to confirm the child's distorted picture of the world and to solidify his already disturbed reaction pattern to authority. The child then evolves elaborate devices for evading situations that he perceives as authoritative and for maneuvering both himself and others in order to avoid them.

The geographical and socio-economic distribution of delinquency tends to confirm the correlation between particular kinds of deprivations and the specific nature of the hostile delinquent act. If certain areas within the community give rise to conditions that increase the likelihood of critical disparities between a child's growth needs and possibilities for satisfying them, it seems reasonable to assume that within such areas there will be a corresponding increase in "amplification or disorganization of the drives into hostile or destructive aggression." [6] In the adolescent, this process culminates in the production of behavior termed delinquent. In the parent, the process seems to lead to attitudes toward children which, in recent years, it has become fashionable to label as "rejecting." Too often, consideration of the parents of the delinquent does not go beyond this kind of pseudo-scientific name-calling. It might be assumed from the lack of awareness of parents and their problems that we believe that the geographic areas with high delinquency rates have atmospheric conditions peculiarly favorable to the production of rejecting parents. A careful study both of indi-

[6] Bender, *op. cit.*, p. 242.

vidual family units and of the epidemiological patterns in particular community areas is needed, if knowledge about the treatment and prevention of delinquency is to advance.

The Parents of Delinquents

Studying the parents of delinquents highlights the dire realities of the setting in which so many of these parents have spent their childhood, are living, and seem destined to remain. Even a cursory survey reveals a complex of economic and social factors that operate to increase the concentration of delinquency: inadequate housing, poor schools, and lack of decent recreational, medical, and other facilities. The pressures of daily existence—in which choice and alternative are crowded out by the struggle for mere survival— mark the lives of many of these adults, as well as of their children. Such parents, when seen in social agencies, are often bitter, disheartened people. Social workers should be exceedingly cautious about labeling, as resistance, defenses that have become essential protective devices to many of these severely traumatized individuals. Because these clients have been dealt with severely by life, they often do not seem to have the strength to participate in well-intentioned efforts to improve their situations. This is true not only in their activity in social agencies, but in their role in the community as well.

Many of these parents can scathingly point out the shocking deficiencies in the facilities within their neighborhood. Yet these same parents are often those who do not participate, much less take leadership, in efforts to improve these conditions. Thus they are deprived of the vitalizing experience of striking back at the forces that are daily thrusting them further into physical and emotional illness. Instead, many of them seem to welter in frustration, guilt, and hostility, which are displaced not only onto their children but (with some cause) onto courts and social agencies as well. Although their anger at a bad school, an inadequate public assistance budget, or racial discrimination is based in reality, it may, in the individual treatment situation, give the appearance of resistance. The worker is tempted so to characterize this reaction because it seems part of the whole effort of the parent to externalize the difficulties that have brought the child to a social agency.

16

Despite the fact that many of these parents are very troubled people themselves, and that some of them may have serious emotional disturbances, they are often reluctant to explore their own difficulties. Some parents would like to separate themselves completely from what they consider to be a humiliating and painful experience brought upon them by their child. Others feel strong guilt about their own real or fancied role in the youngster's delinquency. These problems are encountered in some degree in the parents of all disturbed adolescents. They tend to appear in a more acute form, however, in the parents of delinquents. This may be the result, in part, of the parents' extreme discomfort about the particular nature of the symptoms manifested by their children, and the discomfort is often intensified by the prospect of treatment.

Parents who have judged their own children most severely are often those who are most concerned about coming to an agency, since they fear that their own shortcomings will be brought to light. Sometimes these parents, although insisting that the agency do something for or to their children, either refuse outright to come to the agency themselves or give obviously flimsy excuses for their repeated failure to keep appointments. Some who do keep appointments succeed, nevertheless, in avoiding their involvement in a treatment process. They insist, with righteous indignation, that the adolescent is the one in trouble and that they have no part in it, giving notice in one way or another that they will brook no exploration into their lives.

These parents very often see treatment as a challenge to their own authority over the adolescent and feel that the worker will become a rival. Frequently, improvement in an adolescent's behavior or attitude may precipitate intensified parental resistance, especially in those disturbed families where the "misbehaving" adolescent is used as a convenient scapegoat for the more basic conflict within the family or the family's relationship to the community.[7] The worker has reason to be wary about the parent's participation; even when he pleads desperately for help it does not mean that he is necessarily accessible to treatment. When parents say "help me" they may simply mean that they want the agency to assume responsibility for having the child placed or

[7] Ruth S. Eissler, M.D., "Scapegoats of Society," *Searchlights on Delinquency* (K. R. Eissler, M.D., ed.), International Universities Press, New York, 1949, p. 228.

17

that they desire assistance in forcing him to conform to their demands, some of which may be entirely unacceptable or even intolerable to the adolescent.

The Problem of Etiology

Delinquency, a social infection, is epidemic. The mode of transmission of the pathology is from the community to the family to the individual. All workers, attacking the pathology at one of these different but related points, must understand the interconnections. Study and measurement of processes occurring at these three levels are essential for real understanding of the problem and call for the use of various conceptual and scientific instruments. Since these processes, although representing different levels of integration, are all part of the single complex called society, there can be no question about the need for careful study of their interrelationships. But there can be no facile transposition or mechanical application of concepts from one level to the other.

To demonstrate a simple, direct interrelationship between bad conditions in a neighborhood and severe psychopathology in a particular delinquent child is not easy, even where the connection appears to be a close one. Etiological factors must be followed through various types of social and psychological processes, and sometimes through several families or generations. This is a laborious and painstaking task but one that is essential for an extension of the understanding of delinquent pathology, both of society and of the individuals who comprise it.

Such a three-dimensional grasp of etiology, however, is implicit in many phases of the day-to-day grappling with the exigencies of treatment of the delinquent. Out of such an empirical approach, valuable clues about ways of attacking some of the basic causes of delinquency may emerge. Only by increasing knowledge about both etiology and treatment, at all levels of operation, can real meaning be given to attempts at prevention. Otherwise, the attempts will remain ineffectual and meaningless.

II. An Approach to Treatment

ACKNOWLEDGMENT OF THE IMPORTANCE of precise differential diagnostic thinking about the delinquent ought to be sufficient protection against any "shotgun" approach to treatment. Nonetheless, even though the worker may agree and subscribe to the axioms that every client is different and that each case has its own unique features, there is something about work with delinquents which tends to undermine these very basic and widely accepted tenets.

The very fact that a number of delinquents appear in court together and that it is alleged that they have conjointly engaged in a violation of the law seems to have a most insidious effect on everyone who must deal with these adolescents whether he be judge, probation officer, social worker, or psychiatrist. Something about the very legal categorization of the delinquent tends to thrust all concerned toward an approach in which the treatment is designed to fit the "crime" rather than the individual. The worker with delinquents, therefore, must be especially watchful not to fall into stereotyped thinking about the adolescents who appear in his office despite the sometimes striking similarity in the presenting pictures.

The tendency for the therapeutic approach to be unduly shaped by the act an adolescent has committed, rather than by the nature of the individual he is, may grow partially out of some of the specific techniques required for this type of work. For example, it is sometimes necessary to take account of the symptomatic be-

19

havior of the individual in a somewhat more specific fashion than is the case in work with some of the more classical neurotic types of disturbances. The careful differentiation, however, of the delinquent adolescent from his co-delinquent, or from all those who have committed similar acts, will not in itself lead to sufficient understanding of his problem. It is equally important to keep in mind some of the salient features of delinquency reflected in many of the cases seen.

All those who attempt to help delinquents or their parents must take into account the prominence of the factor of deprivation that appears so strikingly in the history of delinquents. The reading of case after case of unbelievable starvation at many levels —the emotional, the cultural, the educational, and the economic— tempts the worker figuratively to approach all delinquents with an armful of gifts as if their difficulties could somehow be resolved by the appeasement of their many hungers. In a sense, this may not be such a bad general attitude for persons working with delinquents. It must be tempered, however, with a sharp awareness of the many barriers which are interposed between the worker and the adolescent and which will stand in the way of any free or spontaneous interchange between them. Not the least of these, of course, is the way in which the client's prior experience with authoritarian figures often contributes to a suspiciousness and guardedness that cannot be dissolved by even the most permissive therapeutic smile.

Obviously, the difficulties in communicating with delinquents or their parents do not stem from a single cause and are not to be explained in terms of any one factor. Certainly, the silent, unresponsive adolescent who sits inaccessibly across the desk cannot be simply categorized as "withdrawn." The worker must have some awareness of how different this same person would be if the worker had the opportunity of seeing him outside the interview situation—in his own neighborhood or with his own peers. The worker must learn to view with skepticism those psychological reports that may describe an adolescent as being intellectually retarded, unless the examiner has learned to take into account the unbelievably traumatic and distorting effects of the cultural, educational, and emotional deprivations that this adolescent may have undergone as a member of a minority group barely tolerated in the community. Certainly, if he is to have any understanding of the people he is endeavoring to help, the worker in the field of delinquency must guard against trying to explain the behavior of adolescents and their parents in terms of the middle-class values and mores that may be more appropriate to the worker's world than the client's.

Although no good therapist treats his patient in a vacuum, the one who is working with delinquents must be particularly careful to avoid this error. No treatment process is really useful unless it takes into consideration the pressing reality conditions that form the context of the client's life. With the delinquent, this context would seem to be clearly evident and difficult to ignore in view of the kinds of pressure from the court, school, family, and neighbors to which he is often subjected.

Some workers, however, in their efforts to dissociate themselves in the adolescent's mind from such unpleasant forces, commit the error of blinding themselves to their existence and thus sometimes do the adolescent and the community a real disservice. This error is most frequently committed by workers who lack treatment skills or who have not completely resolved their own thinking, identifications, and feelings about their therapeutic role. Actually, it is often advisable for the worker to assume the role of actively protecting the adolescent against reality pressures. Based on the diagnostic and treatment indications, such activity may form an important part of the therapeutic work, especially during the early phases of treatment. When the worker undertakes such a role planfully and with awareness, there is less likelihood that the treatment process will be removed from reality.

Treatment should be conceived as an attempt to provide adolescents and their families with a living experience that takes into account who the client is, the nature of his world, and his particular needs, problems, and strengths. Although each treatment procedure should be based on diagnostic understanding, this is often achieved laboriously in the course of a relationship that should from the outset be therapeutically oriented.

The processes of study, diagnosis, and treatment are not only interrelated in scope but must often be sequentially intertwined.

21

Although therapeutic effects may be achieved in the course of helping efforts on every conceivable level, formal goal-directed psychotherapeutic endeavor requires certain minimal preconditions. First, there must be some systematic attempt to determine the nature and extent of pathology. Second, such an assessment must also evaluate ego strengths and the possibility of establishing with the client a relationship based on the premises necessary to therapeutic work. If an adolescent or parent is reluctant, guarded, or consciously or unconsciously resistive, the nature, extent, and appropriateness of his defenses must be assessed.

For delinquents and their families who have been, are, or may be associated with such authoritative agencies as courts, the establishment of treatment goals must also take into account the use that the agency expects to make of such legal machinery. The possibility of using the court to protect an adolescent in the absence of a parent or guardian who can assume a responsible role in his life must be distinguished from the use of the authority of the court to bring a resistive adolescent within reach of the agency's therapeutic artillery. If the court is to be used as an effective treatment resource, the worker should be aware that he and the delinquent must ultimately engage in a mutual process, even though it does not begin as such.

Conditions for Extramural Treatment

In order to decide whether treatment can be carried on extramurally or not, the intake worker or therapist may have to balance all that is known about the adolescent and his functioning against a host of reality factors. Although the diagnostic evaluation of the delinquent himself will in many cases be the major determinant, there are numerous instances in which a number of seemingly peripheral considerations will have to be given weight. Of crucial importance, in this connection, is a realistic appraisal of the facilities available. It is all very well to say that an adolescent should be treated extramurally, but unless the agency undertaking treatment can provide the skills necessary for working with this particular adolescent, the gesture of "saving him from an institution" will be a pretty empty one. It may be noted here that when it is not possible to give a first appointment until six months or a year after referral, entering the name on a "waiting list" is sometimes worse than not accepting the referral at all in view of the rapid deterioration that so often takes place after an adolescent has been brought to court.

Absurd as it may be to undertake extramural treatment when it is not truly feasible, it is hardly more effective to make the kind of unrealistic recommendation found in so many psychiatric reports that give instructions for placement of the child "in an institutional setting where he may receive psychotherapy." There are very few institutions for delinquents today that offer much in the way of formal psychotherapy. There are, however, an increasing number that offer a therapeutic atmosphere, sometimes including psychiatric consultation, and treatment-oriented services on various levels. For many delinquents who should not remain in the community such placements offer desirable, although limited, alternatives. Nevertheless, even a poor placement may have advantages over "spots" of kindness from a parent or relative or inadequate agency treatment, if there is no continuing or reliable provision for supporting the adolescent in the community. The fact that a rejecting parent or an indifferent school is obviously maneuvering to "get rid" of an adolescent does not mean that there may not be very valid reasons to go ahead with placement, even though one may not accept the rationalizations of the people who are doing the rejecting. Unfortunately, the processes mirrored by the campaign to send the adolescent away often make his remaining in the community unfeasible.

The many cautions directed against inappropriate plans for extramural treatment draw attention to the basic premises underlying the motto inscribed over the entrance to the New York City Court of Domestic Relations, "The Sanctity of the Home— The Integrity of the Family." A poor home, as many workers have learned, is often better for a child than a good institution. Such a statement, however, is a meaningless bromide unless qualified by the concept that the decisions around extramural versus intramural treatment must be governed by the total diagnostic considerations. Such assessment must take account of the adolescent's strengths as well as his pathology, of those forces around him that can be utilized in growth as well as those that are destructive. The adolescent's own evaluation of the situation must be carefully analyzed. An adolescent may perceive parents or adults as rejecting or hostile toward him when such an attitude is far removed from what is actually going on in the adult himself. Even so, the adolescent's view of things cannot be explained away solely as an artifice, since what he perceives does reflect his version of reality even though it may not be an accurate representation of it.

Similarly, when an adolescent clings desperately to what seems to be a really bad home situation, it is not always for neurotic or pathological reasons. He must also be credited with the ability to perceive, in the seemingly rejecting hostile parents, some of the same buried processes that often come to light only after considerable treatment of the parents. Even in some of the most outwardly punitive and hostile parents there is a persistence of positive feeling toward the adolescent in spite of their relative helplessness to resist the forces that almost, despite themselves, push them into being outwardly negativistic toward their child. The recognition of glimmerings of love may not in itself enable the adolescent to tolerate his home, but sometimes it may be enough, with therapeutic intervention, to allow him sufficient elbow room so that he can derive adequate supplementary support outside the home.

The authors believe that it is the reinforcing and cumulative impact of many frustrating and traumatizing experiences which produces the acting-out type of pathology in the adolescent, and that this same process may operate in reverse in contributing to his survival. Sometimes, with just a minimal positive foothold within the home, an adolescent may derive sufficient additional support from secondary sources such as a grandparent, uncle, older sibling, teacher, group worker, or even a fellow gang member, so that he can remain in the community.

To permit the constructive use of such potential assets in delinquent adolescents takes considerable skill on the part of the worker. He may approach the task somewhat more optimistically if he recognizes that sometimes he need only assist in developing the strengths and potentials already there, rather than undertake the overwhelming and usually impossible task of trying to start from scratch to build a positive structure solely within the confines of the therapeutic relationship.

24

A decision to engage in extramural treatment must be based on a careful scrutiny and evaluation of the potentialities for mutual tolerance between the adolescent and his family. Similarly, the chances for an adolescent's survival in the community will be very much influenced by what the possibilities are for his deriving anything positive from the school he attends—the extent to which the school can be expected to put up with him, or can come to terms with his needs. Analogous consideration must be given to the recreational, social, and vocational areas. The mere existence of such possibilities, however, does not assure the probability that they will be utilized by the adolescent.

In this connection, it is perhaps important to mention a factor that is often not specifically included in the diagnostic appraisal, that is, the degree of organization or disorganization in the over-all functioning of the individual. When the entire history and context of the adolescent's life tend to undermine the development of even the most elementary kind of structure, assistance in any single life area may not be too helpful since, in the absence of adequate structural patterning, constructive experiences cannot be utilized as a base for subsequent opportunities for growth.

The kind of prognostic judgment required of a therapist working with delinquents must be supported by concrete knowledge of the socio-cultural milieu in which his clients operate. For example, trying to understand or to be useful to a client within the relevant context of his social and material reality if he is a member of a minority group in our culture is exceedingly difficult without specific knowledge of the life, cultural patterns, and problems of such groups. Similarly, the worker's ability to help certain adolescents will be greatly influenced by the extent of his knowledge about gangs, or possibly even some specific data about the particular teen-age gang to which a particular adolescent either owes his allegiance or from which he may have been excluded.

Role of the Therapy Group

Therapy groups often provide a kind of rough instrument for catching glimpses of both the adolescent and his parents in a social context which elude the therapist in the individual interview situation. One clue to the probable importance of the place of

25

group therapy in an agency's treatment armamentarium is suggested by the strikingly different impressions received about the adolescent and his parents as they are observed in individual and group treatment. The most obvious factor accounting for this difference is the radical alteration in both authority and dependency patterns as they evolve between the therapist and client in the group setting. The mere fact that the group therapist is outnumbered by the adolescent (or parent) and his peers frequently has a dramatic impact on the over-all attitudes of the clients toward the therapist, and vice versa. There is a freedom about openly acknowledging and sometimes overtly expressing feelings in the group situation which often appears only during the latter phases of individual treatment. The group not only tends to be strongly supportive about the expression of negative feelings, but it also permits the adolescent or parent to express positive feeling or to reach out and accept help from an authority figure at a time when it might be too threatening for either to do so if confronted by the therapist alone.

Whether or not such differences between individual and group treatment may actually be used to the client's advantage in group therapy depends on the diagnostic picture. Some adolescents and parents who are obviously more comfortable in the group are also more inaccessible there, and may even use the group as a kind of hiding place where they can go through the motions of treatment without actually becoming involved at all. In such instances, the only professional consolation is in the assurance that the group may be used to establish a contact that can prepare the client for individual psychotherapy. In some instances, the discovery is made that an entirely different approach should have been used in the first place; that probably the only effective medium would be intensive psychoanalytic treatment, or that vocational guidance is the adolescent's initial and most pressing need.

In the field of group therapy one question requiring further study concerns the possibility of establishing differential criteria for group versus individual treatment. Our work at the clinic indicates that an initial group experience for either parents or adolescents rarely seems to work counter to moving forward in subsequent individual treatment. The worker, however, must be sufficiently alert and flexible so that those who ought not to continue in group therapy can either be shifted to individual treatment or be helped in other appropriate ways. However, even relatively brief group experience may sometimes provide important supplementary diagnostic data or assist in the resolution of certain crucial situations.[1]

The therapy groups provide important kinds of understanding about the group life of adolescents and parents who are being seen in individual and group treatment. It is true that most of the disturbances in behavior which come within the province of casework and psychiatry represent disruptions in the individual's group relationships. The use of the group process, therefore, in the treatment of clients seen in the field of delinquency may be of special importance because of the direct way that some of their difficulties appear to be related to breakdowns in the social institutions that are supposedly designed to serve them. For many of these adolescents and their parents, the re-establishment of mental health will depend upon the extent to which they achieve some competence in grappling with those forces that are thrusting them toward pathology. To deal with these problems they will in most cases need the assistance of their peers. Therefore, whenever the level of treatment permits the strengthening of the ties that bind them to their fellows, an important contribution is made to their ultimate survival and adjustment.

Determining the Nature of the Treatment

It often requires the most careful clinical judgment to know when a particular disturbance in an adolescent's life situation can be approached directly and when the handling of it must be deferred until certain crucial changes have been brought about in his characteristic mode of operation. To know when and how to deal with or call attention to transference phenomena, whether to select individual rather than group treatment, or some combination thereof, all requires considerable diagnostic skill and

[1] See the chapter on The Intake Process, p. 29; also Martin L in the chapter on Group Therapy for Adolescents, p. 69.

27

experience, and in many instances the full scrutiny of a multidiscipline clinical team.

Continuing awareness of all of these considerations should lead to some recognition of the limitations of, and give some perspective to, such time-honored therapeutic devices as interpreting behavior solely in the light of transference distortions or seeing treatment simply as the ventilation of the client's concealed hostility. Certainly, the relatively few treatment hours spent with the client must be seen within the framework of the all-encompassing life dislocations to which he is so often exposed. If it is recognized that therapeutic efforts are in some instances a rather poor substitute for more relevant or comprehensive changes (which may simply not be possible), then at least the worker may attempt as total an approach as facilities permit to the problem confronting the client.

Sometimes it is possible for treatment to act as a kind of springboard that assists these families to utilize more effectively community services that were previously inaccessible. In any event, the worker should most certainly avoid being placed in that dubious position in which questionable psychotherapeutic efforts are exerted in lieu of badly needed concrete services. The worker's or the agency's efforts should really be but one part of a total, integrated community effort to assist families that are deteriorating because of the absence of certain vital community services. Even when it is not possible to succeed in rallying all the concrete assistance that so many of these families require, and a more narrow area is selected perforce for the focus of treatment, it is nevertheless important that the adolescent and his family be viewed continually in relation to their world.

III. The Intake Process

THE PROBLEM OF ESTABLISHING a helping relationship with a delinquent obviously presents many difficulties. In addition to his particular resistances that emanate from, and contribute to, the pathological process, the delinquent has many reality reasons for wishing to avoid involvement in a treatment relationship.

An adolescent who has been the subject of a court hearing and has been adjudged delinquent—and perhaps has spent some time either in a detention home or on probation—is inevitably oriented to a legalistic and authoritarian approach. He has been in a situation where he has had to defend himself against a number of persons who have the power to impose punishment. Therefore, when treatment is suggested—perhaps as the result of a psychiatric study by the court or a detention home or a psychiatric hospital—he understandably is confused and wary. In reality, he often must relate both to the court and to the treatment service. For example, although he may be relieved of a formal check on his adherence to the rules of probation, he knows that he will have to reappear in court in the event of subsequent delinquency.

The delinquent also has many reasons to be uneasy about discussing his activities. The clinic worker should at the outset explain to him what material can be considered confidential and what he will or will not use in reporting to the court, particularly in the instance of a subsequent hearing. Confidentiality in this context is difficult to delineate and even more difficult for the delinquent to grasp and accept. In the same way, the adolescent may be told that he has "freedom of choice" as to whether he chooses probation or clinic treatment. He knows, however, that repeated breaking of clinic appointments, like failing to see the probation officer at regular intervals, brings the same result—another court hearing.

A delinquent who is referred by a court to a treatment service inevitably associates the treatment agency with the court. Even when the agency has no formal administrative connection with the court and is physically separate from it, the adolescent views the service as an extension of the legal authority. Although the distinctions of aim and responsibility may be explained to him in the intake interview, his confusions and suspicions usually will not be materially allayed; their ultimate resolution is a part of the treatment process itself.

If a clinic is structurally a part of the court and is located in the same building, an intensification of the adolescent's confusion and distrust may be expected. By virtue of the physical proximity of the clinic to the court, the intake interviews, as well as all subsequent contacts, are associated in the delinquent's mind with his courtroom experiences. Legal requirements that give delinquent or neglected children probation status during the period of treatment—although the clinic worker instead of the probation officer carries the *de facto* responsibility to the court—tend further to link the clinic to the probation department. If the worker is unable to engage the adolescent in treatment and the latter repeatedly fails to keep appointments, action on the part of the court may be required. For all these reasons a court clinic is not a "neutral" therapeutic setting. On the contrary, because it is allied with authority it arouses in the adolescent and his parents the same strong feelings of apprehension that were engendered by the investigation, the court hearing, and the psychiatric examination that preceded the referral to the clinic.

The adolescent often is prepared for referral to the clinic by the psychiatrist, the probation officer, or the detention home social worker who recommends such treatment. When he arrives for the intake interview, however, he is generally confused about the reason for his referral. In the majority of cases, he wonders whether his presence at the clinic means that he is "crazy," "dumb," or

30

physically ill. Sometimes he asks whether he will actually live at the clinic, whether he will be given medicine, "shots," or more psychological tests.

ALICE T

Alice, 13, was referred to the clinic by the judge. Although she seemed somewhat withdrawn and lacking in feeling, she did express directly a fear that she was "crazy." She had been brought into court for stabbing a 14-year-old boy who had attempted to snatch her purse. Previous to this episode, which had brought her to the attention of the court, her life had been characterized by patterns of seeming conformity. She had been placed in three foster homes before she was 6. Her parents' stated reason for placement was that they were unemployed and could not support her. She had returned to her own home when she was 10 and during her first year at home a younger brother was born. Her teachers and her parents said that she daydreamed excessively and had increasing difficulty in keeping up with her school work. The psychiatrist thought that there was no evidence of an active schizophrenic process at the time of the examination and recommended further exploration, with a view to treatment.

The intake worker attempted to handle Alice's anxiety and fear directly, stressing the fact that Alice needed help rather than punishment and that she would have the opportunity of talking further with the worker about such things as her fear of being crazy. The challenging approach of the intake worker did not, of course, eradicate the girl's guilt and anxiety. It did, however, sufficiently correct her preconceptions and distortions so that treatment could proceed.

The Intake Interview

The intake worker should have clear and specific knowledge of the reasons why the adolescent is referred for treatment. The delinquent should generally be made aware, at the outset, that the worker knows about the incident that brought the child into court. The worker should be not judgmental but factual. He

31

should be accepting of the adolescent but not of his delinquent acts. He should be friendly and warm but must avoid the trap of aligning himself with the adolescent as a co-delinquent.

The intake worker usually has in his possession a mass of data about the delinquent and his family, only part of which may be considered valid social history. The factual material often can be used as the starting point for a focused interview and for clarifying the current problem of the adolescent. If the adolescent has already talked to others about his family, his living arrangements, and his school situation, *ad nauseam,* no purpose is served by merely reviewing the facts. The worker, instead, should introduce some relevant point from the court reports or psychiatric examinations which has a diagnostic or treatment implication. For example, reference may be made to school difficulties or crowded or inadequate housing conditions mentioned in a report, but it should be done in such a way as to reveal the worker's concern about the effects of these circumstances on the child. Similarly, there is no point in referring to facts about delinquent activities cited in the petition unless the worker does so for a specific purpose, such as to give the adolescent an opportunity to express his feeling about the way these matters have been handled by others and to make clear the worker's different attitude toward the child.

The intake worker should endeavor to discover, in the reports of teachers or probation officers, or in the descriptions of the way the adolescent behaved at court hearings—which are usually part of the social history sent to the treatment agency—something about the adolescent's characteristic behavior patterns. Of special importance are the attitudes and feelings he evokes or provokes in the adults with whom he comes into contact. In his initial contact with the worker he will expect, and sometimes even demand, a certain type of adult reaction to which he previously has made some kind of adaptation. If he is accustomed to a good deal of rejection, acceptance in too large a dose will not seem genuine to him. In the same way, too much seeming permissiveness on the part of the worker may threaten an adolescent whose defenses require that he operate in a world that is "managed." The adolescent's tolerance for personal relationships must also be appraised if the worker is to avoid the mistake of overwhelming him with expressions of positive feeling which, at the moment, may only be frightening. Such disciplined exercise of therapeutic restraint is predicated on the worker's awareness of his patient's needs and of his own reactions. He must learn not to respond negatively to either seductive or provocative behavior on the part of the adolescent.

In the course of the intake interview, the worker needs to use the whole gamut of interviewing skills to achieve the participation —beyond yes or no answers—of the delinquent. Since the adolescent's previous relationships, particularly in court, have made him acutely conscious of the authoritarian nature of the probation officer's function, even minimum participation on his part indicates some movement. Only if the worker is secure enough to recognize the adolescent's ambivalence, not only about the court experience and his referral for treatment but about the actual intake interview process itself, is there much hope of securing a real feeling response.

Some adolescents view the treatment agency from the outset as a place of refuge and help. Because they do not have too many distortions of feeling as a result of their previous experiences with parents, siblings, schools, or courts, they enter into a positive relationship with relative ease. Other young people, however, think of treatment as a new form of adult control and punishment and react to the experience strongly and negatively. If they continue contact even for a short period, they usually do so because of the vastly more threatening demands in their total life situation. But delinquent patients—like all patients—begin treatment with both negative and positive reactions, which they express in a variety of ways during the intake interview. This ambivalence, which undoubtedly has strong negative elements with the delinquent group, must be recognized and dealt with then and subsequently. If, in the initial contact, the worker precipitously threatens the client's defenses so that he becomes convinced that treatment is pressing him toward changes he is unready or unwilling to face, he may withdraw entirely.

Sometimes the mere mention by the worker of the frequency of treatment contacts may, in itself, mobilize so much anxiety and

33

be so threatening as to cause the adolescent to decide against treatment. The worker, in planning treatment for each individual, should be aware of the necessity to be flexible about appointments, aware of the possible limitations in the adolescent's attention span, and sensitive to his particular tolerance for frustration. If, after all these precautions have been taken, the adolescent still refuses the proffered help, it may mean that this avenue of help is, at least for the present, closed to him. He sometimes must choose the known, with its obvious discomforts, to the unknown, which may seem to him a vastly more threatening alternative.

LARRY S

Larry, a 14-year-old boy who was brought into the court by his mother because of his refusal to attend school, could not accept clinic help. He had apparently not shown overt problem behavior either at school or at home until his mother became pregnant when he was 13. The child guidance clinic to which he was referred for study reported that he had an I.Q. of 117. He had marked anxiety about his own sexual adequacy, however, and this seemed to have been accentuated by his mother's pregnancy. His neurotic fears increased, as did his truancy and the stealing of small sums from his mother's purse, just before his sister's birth. All these symptoms, however, had abated somewhat by the time the sister was about two months old. At this point Larry was referred to the court clinic for treatment. The school and the child guidance clinic believed that his problems, even though they were not currently being expressed in symptomatic behavior, were nevertheless of a serious nature.

Larry had some awareness of the basis for the referral but during the intake interview he definitely said that he could not talk about his feelings "without having to go out and get into trouble." Since he was still on probation he chose to report to the probation officer at regular intervals, refusing to consider treatment and saying that if in the future he felt he needed help he would come back to the clinic. Larry's response to the offer of psychiatric help seemed to indicate that he had few defenses against his anxiety, and that he equated treatment with a drive to engage in delinquent acts.

34

Initial Resistance

Understanding the initial resistance of delinquents is important diagnostically. As with any client, it may be an indication of how deep-rooted or how near the surface the conflictual matrix is. With delinquent adolescents, however, acute initial resistance is not necessarily an inseparable part of the adolescent's central problem. Only if resistance is seen in its relation to the total personality and as a *modus vivendi* in the adolescent's dilemma, can it be correctly assessed. Resistance may be of such a nature that treatment is not feasible. On the other hand, it may yield to fairly simple, direct handling. A few children were taken on for treatment at the clinic in the face of their expressed unwillingness to accept help. For the most part, these were adolescents who desperately needed treatment and who seemed capable of establishing a relationship and utilizing help if their initial resistance could be resolved.

The necessity for taking an active role in getting such adolescents to accept treatment has long been recognized, but is currently being re-emphasized. The assumption that the consent of client or patient is essential to effective help has perhaps been too literally interpreted by some agencies. Caseworkers and psychiatrists who have worked with delinquent groups recognize that the principle of choice must be modified when the adult or child is unable to care for himself and requires the protective services of the community. For example, if a child is institutionalized, the matter of choice almost ceases to operate. He is "treated" with the available institutional facilities. Experience indicates that he responds to various therapeutic techniques if they have a sound diagnostic basis. In the same way, delinquent adolescents who have admittedly grave prognoses are sometimes able to respond to protective therapeutic services in an extramural setting. The required techniques, which include a strong element of direction, are not always too familiar to caseworkers in non-authoritarian settings. If these clients are to be kept in treatment, they must be made to realize the necessity for coming regularly to the clinic and to feel that the worker "insists" upon their keeping appointments.

JANET R

Janet, 15, was typical of these adolescents who endeavor to evade treatment. She looked at least 18 when she came into the clinic. Her mother had died when she was 3 and Janet lived with her father and stepmother. She had five older siblings all living away from home. Her father was an alcoholic who beat her whenever he was drunk. Her stepmother for a number of years had seemed threatened by Janet's superior intellectual functioning as well as by her physical maturity. Janet had done well in a neighborhood school (she had an I.Q. of 137) but during her first year in a high school in another borough she seemed unable to find her place with the group. She ran away from home eighteen times in a year and was then referred to the court. While she was at a detention home, she was seen by a psychiatrist who made a diagnosis of psychoneurosis with phobic traits and excessive dependency needs. As a result, clinic treatment was suggested rather than institutionalization.

She told the intake worker at the clinic that she did not want treatment and that she would probably run away before the next appointment. The worker told Janet that the clinic had accepted her and expected her to keep the appointment, and stressed the fact that the worker was interested in helping her and would see her regularly once a week, or oftener if necessary. Janet responded to these overtures positively; she managed to keep her appointment with the psychiatrist and to keep regular weekly appointments for three months. She then told the worker that she could not face things any longer at home or at school (and presumably in treatment). She again ran away, this time to a married brother's home in Chicago. When he sent her back to New York, she returned to the clinic immediately and remained in treatment for another six months. Janet subsequently said she would prefer placement in an institutional setting, as a "protection against running away." This was arranged, with planning done step by step. The clinic recognized that Janet doubtless sought some self-punishment in this plan and was also motivated by the wish to find a setting that would provide satisfactions on an infantile level. The prognosis for Janet must be guarded. Resolute handling of her initial resistance to treatment, however, made it possible to plan placement with her on a more dynamic and hopeful basis.

The Parents

When treatment facilities are limited the focus of community interest tends to be largely on the adolescent himself. If the parents are not treated, however, therapeutic results with the adolescent are in many instances negligible. Various factors enter into the selection of parents for treatment. The role that the parents play in the adolescent's life is the chief consideration. The role is related to the chronological age of the child as well as to the nature of the parent-child relationship. Obviously, a mother usually has more points of physical and psychological contact with an 8-year-old child than she does with the average teen-ager. The need for treatment of a parent who is interfering with the healthy development of a relatively young child can hardly be questioned. The parent of the adolescent is equally in need of treatment when the adolescent is exposed to gross parental neglect and extreme infantilization.

The parents of delinquents, when they are drawn into treatment, react to the treatment facility in a variety of ways. They may attempt to use the agency only as an extension of their own punitive drives. On the other hand, they may use its permissive atmosphere to avoid facing their own and the child's real difficulties.

The parent's reaction to the referral for treatment for himself may be paraphrased thus, "I am not the delinquent; why must I come here?" The very vehemence, however, of his denial of involvement in his child's difficulties may often conceal his underlying concern about his own part in contributing to the delinquency. The acting-out behavior of adolescents obviously often reflects disturbances in parent-child relationships. The adolescent actually may be pushed into delinquency by overt or unconscious parental provocation. Often the delinquent pattern appears to be kept alive in order to maintain an unstable family equilibrium.

Many of the parents manifest considerable guilt, which is natural enough since many have treated their children quite miserably. These same parents, however, often seem unable to identify with the adolescent and his difficulties. In such instances one often finds that their guilt is directly tied to their own early fantasies, however distant they may be. The court experience and the subsequent treatment contacts are frequently utilized by them primarily to meet their personal needs and frustrations, while the adolescent and his delinquency are thrust into the background. Frequently these parents have distortions in their relationships—analogous to their inappropriate reactions to their children—with their own parents or with their marital partners. On the job or in the home, they are hampered by the same unresolved problems that interfere with their relationships to their children. It appears that it is equally difficult for them to function in the community for their own or the neighborhood's benefit. The burden of their inner conflicts, and of the overwhelming economic and social circumstances with which so many of these parents are confronted, often overshadows the problem of the adolescent's delinquency. The delinquency is, in fact, only a minor reflection of a whole series of destructive happenings that have beset the family for years.

The intake worker, at the time that he interviews the parents, may have superficial information about them. The probation officer's report and other records usually tell little beyond the age, marital status, employment, and current economic status of the family. The adequacy of the intake interview with the parent, therefore, will depend on the worker's ability to identify with the parent and his problems, and to elicit material that will aid in evaluating his assets and limitations. The worker's sensitivity to the parent's reaction to the whole court experience is of major importance and often influences the ultimate outcome of the treatment of both parent and child. During the intake interview, many parents first show their resistance to involvement in the treatment process. Unless such resistance is recognized and handled, it may prove impossible ever to engage the parent in treatment. He will remain a shadowy, peripheral figure or will interpose himself between the adolescent and the clinic so that neither the delinquent nor the parent himself can obtain even minimal help. If, however, the resistance is recognized and dealt with as such from the very beginning it may be worked through sufficiently to enable him to proceed with and use treatment.

The parents of delinquents who enter into treatment may wish to use the agency for purposes that may not be compatible with the objectives of treatment but that may be related to them. Those who bring their child to court because he is disobedient and beyond their control may view the treatment agency—as they do the court —as the strong arm of the law which will effectively buttress their parental dicta. Such use of the court or clinic may also be made by those parents who have unconsciously driven the adolescent into delinquency that resulted in court action. Both groups of parents will make known in the intake interview their feelings about the child and the role they wish the agency to play, perhaps in stronger fashion than they did at the court hearings. If they are seeking a means of punishing the child, they already are disappointed since the judge or probation officer has implied that the child does not need force but treatment. The court action, instead of confirming the parents' attempt to control or punish the adolescent, has precipitated him into a deeply disturbing and anxiety-provoking situation. By the time the parent reaches the treatment agency, his defenses are likely to be strongly mobilized.

With the parent, as with the child, the worker must appraise the nature of the resistance. The parent's recourse or passive resort to the court may be a reflection of his own unresolved difficulties with authority. He may be using the court as a kind of all-powerful parent in the expectation that if he (and his child) could be sufficiently conforming and docile, all his problems would be miraculously dissipated. For some parents, the use of the authority element is the only help that their emotional conflicts permit them to accept. If the adolescent is kept by court order on strict probation, the parents may make a precarious adjustment. Or they may contribute to the adolescent's continued delinquency until finally he is placed in a correctional institution. Often placement, punitively imposed, is the only action that they feel will vindicate them and their whole relationship to the adolescent.

If, in the course of the intake interview, a parent is helped to begin to view the treatment agency in a way that is relatively free from excessive authoritarian-punitive distortions, he may see a way of making use of a therapeutic relationship to change some of the factors in the parent-child relationship which bear directly on the adolescent's delinquency. It must be emphasized, however, that

39

even when this occurs, access has been gained to only a small segment of what is usually a complex, multi-faceted process. The pathological nature of the relationship of the parent to his child is generally only one of many disturbed areas in the psychological, social, and economic life of many of these families. An awareness, at intake, of the possible treatment limitations need not be discouraging if the venture is viewed as one on which the child, the family, and the social agency are embarking together, not to find a cure-all but to take some initial but important steps in bettering the life of the family members with each other and in the community. Even if the distance covered is short, the venture will be well worth the effort if the parent and child move toward more effective social functioning and toward establishing better relationships with people.

IV. Individual Treatment

THE GENERAL APPROACH to clients and the selection of treatment techniques obviously are influenced by the particular function of a social agency. When the treatment of delinquency is the special function, the agency's procedures will differ from those generally applied in an agency with a non-delinquent case load, even though the basic treatment method and the underlying psychological premises are much the same in both settings. In a children's court clinic, for example, where there is a high concentration of a certain type of pathology, a particular kind of initial response on the part of the therapist is indicated. With few exceptions the adolescents referred to the clinic are expressing their disturbances in acting-out behavior, with its accompanying antagonisms to persons in authority. They reach the clinic via the court and this fact alone induces negative attitudes that must be handled at the outset.

If treatment is to be appropriate to the delinquent's particular needs, it must be a fluid process continuously modified to meet the change in his social situation and in his feelings. The life situation of the delinquent must be carefully related to the clinical findings that emerge in the interview setting. His responses to the treatment situation can have little meaning unless they are viewed within the framework of the many momentous and often overwhelming experiences with which he must cope. Unlike patients whose tensions are largely internal, the delinquent may not find great support in a few therapeutic sessions. One or two treatment hours a week may have only this arithmetically proportional influence on him, since he is exposed during the remainder of the week to critical situations that counteract and often nullify the therapeutic influence.

Effective treatment for the delinquent as well as for others requires that the patient be helped to achieve an emotional experience that he has been unable to find, or accept, elsewhere. The delinquent as a rule has failed to establish a satisfactory relationship with a parent figure—a relationship in which he has felt approved and accepted and free to express hostility without fear of punishment or reprisal. To establish a relationship with these hurt and fearful adolescents whose experiences with adults have been chiefly negative is a most difficult therapeutic task. Their defensive and hostile reaction to their recent court experience obviously adds to the problems involved in establishing initial rapport. The approach, therefore, must be as non-threatening as possible.

The case of Mary J illustrates both the extent of pathology and the involved authority-dependency problem which are present in many delinquent adolescents.

Mary J

Mary, 15½, showed marked distrust, hostility, and resentment when she was interviewed at the clinic. She had been brought into court by the Society for the Prevention of Cruelty to Children because she had given birth to an out-of-wedlock baby. Before Mary's appearance at court, her parents had arranged with their family physician to place the baby in an adoptive home, while Mary continued to live with her parents. The judge, noting Mary's acute anxiety, referred her for psychiatric examination. The psychiatrist described her as anxious and guilt ridden; a diagnosis of psychoneurosis, hysterical type, was made. Psychiatric treatment was recommended.

Mary had been subjected to almost incredible rejection by her family. Her mother, the dominant figure in the family, had allied herself with an older son John, 29, who still lived at home The father allied himself with Mary as much as he dared. Peter, 17, also lived at home. Three of Mary's siblings, two brothers and a sister, were married and away from the home. Mary, as the youngest, had been tyrannized by her mother and the older siblings, particularly John.

When Mary was referred to the clinic, no member of her family was willing to continue contact. The mother and John made it clear in their interviews with the intake worker that they expected the court to exercise a restrictive role—actually to carry out their own punitive feelings. Mrs. J did her utmost to terminate Mary's relationship with the clinic, even making an unsuccessful attempt to get the family minister to forbid the contact. Mrs. J impressed the worker as an extremely rigid and compulsive person, with so much hostility toward Mary that she had blocked every normal step Mary had taken as an adolescent in the growing-up process. When ordinary suppressive measures failed, Mrs. J had used her ill health to increase her daughter's guilt and to curb further movement toward independence. She stated several times that she did not like girls, had never wanted any of her own, and had been sure ever since Mary's birth that she would "disgrace" the family.

At the clinic Mary was placed in an intake group,[1] since this setting seemed to provide a less threatening experience than a direct relationship with an adult. It was decided after a few sessions, however, that individual treatment would be the more desirable method. When Mary was first seen by her worker she was still apprehensive and under a great deal of tension. She had a tic in her right eye which she attempted to conceal. In discussing the placement of her baby she seemed to equate this experience with the abandonment of her by David, the baby's father. She said that if she could not have the baby she would have "lost two people."

Mary had known David a brief time and had had sexual relations with him only twice. When she had discovered that she was pregnant and had informed David, he had refused to see her or take any responsibility.

In the interview, she expressed a wish to have her baby back with her, but her planning was markedly unrealistic. She said she believed that she and the baby could live with one of her three

[1] See chapter on Use of Groups in the Intake Process, p. 120.

married siblings. (At the court hearing, her sister and the other members of the family had made it clear they would not take in either Mary or the baby.) The worker told Mary that she knew Mary was fearful about what the clinic might do, and also emphasized her interest in helping Mary work out plans for herself and her baby. A sufficiently meaningful relationship was established that Mary consented to return for regular interviews. The worker was warm, supportive, and realistic about the practical problems.

Mary continued to visit her baby regularly during the first three months of treatment. When the probation department confirmed Mary's report that the baby was not getting adequate care, the clinic worker and the psychiatrist conferred with the couple who had been "given" the baby by Mary's family and physician. The couple refused to release the child, and the clinic, with the aid of the probation department, helped Mary obtain the services of a lawyer in an effort to have the child removed from this home. The case was heard in Supreme Court but the judge refused to release the child and supported the action of Mary's family in placing it. Mary was depressed but her reaction did not seem to be out of proportion to the circumstances. In the next few weeks she obtained a job in a small hat shop and also made arrangements with her lawyer for a rehearing of the case, asking this time for custody of the child. She assumed responsibility for paying his fee. When the case was heard again, Mary was denied custody but the baby was removed from the first home and placed in a foster home supervised by a social agency.

The family continued to exert pressure to prevent Mary from obtaining custody of her child. Her mother became seriously ill during this period and she, as well as Mary's siblings, accused Mary of being responsible for her mother's illness. Mary's guilt was intensified and as a result it became increasingly difficult for her to maintain the rather tenuous stability she had achieved during the earlier period of treatment. Her family at times prevented her from attending clinic and also refused to let her have any outside contacts. At one point the family even had the telephone removed and literally kept her a prisoner.

In spite of the family's punishing attitudes, Mary insisted that she intended to remain at home until she was 18 years old. She felt a girl could be "free" at that age. It was clear that she had determined to suppress her normal adolescent needs and her open resentment of control while she remained at home. The struggle between herself and her family reached such intensity, however, that Mary, after a particularly severe family quarrel, had an attack of amnesia and was taken to a psychiatric hospital. The attending psychiatrist diagnosed it as a hysterical attack in response to her unbearable situation. Mary decided, after consulting with the hospital psychiatrist and subsequently with her caseworker, to remain in the hospital until the worker was able to find a place for her in a working girls' residence.

Mary continued in treatment for eighteen months. In that time she made sufficient progress and achieved enough strength to go ahead with a plan for foster home placement of the baby. She made it clear to her family that she wanted her baby in a supervised home where she could visit it and be known as the child's mother. She made regular financial contributions for board, with a view to assuming eventually full responsibility for the child.

The treatment at the beginning was centered on making plans for the baby. This practical approach enabled Mary to think of the worker as a helpful and supportive person. The experience provided her with the opportunity to feel, for the first time, that not all adults were allied against her and to begin to examine her projections onto all adults of her hostile feelings toward her family. Her continuing relationship with the clinic worker, which met some of her needs for release, support, clarification, and guidance, made it possible for her to function in a reasonably effective way in the face of severe difficulties which, at an earlier point, had completely paralyzed her. Although she was literally surrounded by authoritarian, hostile, and punitive persons at home, she was nonetheless able, with the clinic's help, to cope with them more adequately. In so doing, she achieved a significant alteration in her over-all way of functioning and in her life status.

Mary is representative of a large group of adolescents whose contact with and feelings about the court add a serious complication to an already difficult therapeutic problem. Their suspicion and distrust of the worker and the agency tend to stimulate negative responses. The worker, however, must learn to deal with his own feelings of frustration and annoyance, and not permit them to interfere with the therapeutic opportunity. It is important to remember that the court experience, in addition to intensifying the adolescent's resistance, may also, for the moment, expose and make accessible for treatment his concealed feelings about authority, his struggle between dependence and independence, and his capacity for mobilizing his defenses. The worker must be prepared to go slowly and to anticipate relatively little movement at the outset. Special precautions must be taken to ensure the establishment and maintenance of a positive relationship if treatment is to proceed at all. As the relationship develops, the adolescent's negative responses must be carefully controlled therapeutically, since most of these young people have little capacity to tolerate sustained anxiety.

Setting Therapeutic Goals

In attempting to set therapeutic goals, the worker must be aware of the multitude of personal, social, and cultural factors that are operating in the lives of these young people who are in trouble with and distrustful of most of the accepted community institutions. Usually a wide disparity exists between the value system of this group of deprived adolescents and that of the general community. Many of these adolescents, for example, have had frustrating and unhappy school experiences and they therefore are likely to look with disdain upon regulations about compulsory school attendance. In order to work with a youngster on such matters as regular school attendance, employment, recreation, and so forth, the worker must endeavor to learn something of the adolescent's own values and goals, and of the extent to which these values conform with the standards of the community and with the worker's own.

In working with delinquents, certain values must be affirmed and certain limits must be set. But there is a difference between setting limits and imposing restrictions. Setting limits is a therapeutic device, based on diagnostic considerations. Therapeutic limits, as opposed to authoritative restrictions, take cognizance of the changing needs of the adolescent within his total life situation. They are flexible and geared to the client's capacity to handle certain aspects of his behavior. Thus, at one point it would be entirely compatible with the treatment aim to have an adolescent brought to court for violation of probation, while at another time —when an effort is being made to help him understand the meaning of his acts—such action would be counter-indicated. Within the context of therapy, authority should not be exercised arbitrarily. It must be used discriminately to further the over-all aim of treatment.

Although resistance usually is manifested at the outset of treatment, it may not appear until the adolescent has been in treatment for several weeks or months. When it occurs concomitantly with the growth of a positive relationship, it usually has special significance. The resistance then embodies the defenses that the adolescent has erected against his striving for positive relationships with other adults. It is important for the worker to understand the meaning of the resistance and, through sensitive handling of the defenses, to keep the adolescent in treatment. This phase of treatment offers real opportunity to help the patient work through his resistance and gain some awareness of his defensive patterns.

The treatment goal obviously is influenced by many diagnostic elements—clinical, social, cultural, and familial. The capacity of an adolescent to enter into a treatment relationship depends not only on the extent and nature of his particular pathology but also on his total dynamic status. His external situation and his inner psychological struggle form an interacting unit. The various elements must be appraised and often must be dealt with in some sort of rotation, if not simultaneously.

As has been indicated, the adolescents seen at the clinic represented a range of pathology, including the usual diagnostic entities as well as many permutations of these. From the point of view of treatment, two general approaches seemed to emerge. When the adolescent's pathology seemed to be primarily neurotic, effort was made to understand the underlying processes that led to the symptom of delinquent behavior, with particular interest in the specific character of his traumatic experiences. On the other hand,

47

when the adolescent's disturbance was diagnosed as a severe character disorder or when he seemed to have strong psychopathic trends, attention was focused on the specific nature of the delinquent behavior.

The rationale for the two approaches was the same; that is, the intent was to discover the etiology of the disturbance. In the second group, an understanding of the character of their delinquent behavior usually revealed the nature of their deprivations and traumata. The origin of such pathology is generally in the pre-oedipal period and the developmental processes are generally arrested at this level. As a result, adolescents in this group, for the most part, have not incorporated the accepted value systems, have relatively little guilt when they fail to conform, and tend to experience anxiety only in response to the acute situations into which their faulty character development precipitates them. An explanation, therefore, of their delinquent acts and of their reactions to them and to the court experiences usually provides the essential data to establish a diagnosis.

Sometimes these adolescents with faulty character development show a transient pseudo-anxiety at the time of their appearance in court. However, it usually has been repressed by the time they reach the clinic. When an attempt is made to refer them to other community resources, their defenses are again operating so smoothly that contact generally cannot be established. A therapeutic relationship seems to be extremely difficult to achieve outside an institution. An example of the problem of establishing contact will be presented. In this instance, the symptomatic behavior was not correctly diagnosed, and the boy's defenses were such that it was not possible to treat him in the clinic.

HAROLD R

Harold, 15½, was brought into children's court charged with the possession of a revolver. He had previously been taken to court in Texas for stealing fifty dollars and a car. He had a long history of running away from home, of poor adjustment in school, and of minor delinquencies. He had been previously referred to a school child-guidance clinic because of his lack of interest in school work, his markedly disheveled personal appearance, and his inability to relate to children in his own age group; his companions were usually older girls and boys. In the diagnostic study at the child guidance clinic he scored 98 in the intelligence test, which was felt to be reasonably accurate. He had a well-established pattern of egocentricity which, it was felt, enabled him to form loyalties and allegiances of the gang type rather than constructive relationships. He was thought to have a severe character disorder with marked psychopathic trends. Placement in an institution had been recommended.

When Harold was interviewed at the court clinic, he semed to be extremely anxious. He talked with what seemed to be appropriate affect of his desire for help with his feelings about his family situation. Accordingly, the worker undertook to continue contact with him and to see if some adjustments could be worked out in the family. Harold used subsequent treatment interviews to express considerable hostility and resentment against his parents and the school for the restrictions placed upon him. His anxiety decreased as soon as placement no longer seemed imminent. Whenever an attempt was made to help him discuss his personal problems and conflicts, he manifested considerable defensiveness and blocking. During this time, there were acting-out episodes at home and at school, and also at the clinic.

Concurrently, the worker was endeavoring to lessen the reality pressures to which Harold was being subjected. He was transferred to a vocational school and the parents were seen regularly in an effort to help them relax their demands for rigid conformity from Harold. This they were able to do to a limited extent. For example, they consented to a change of bedtime for Harold—from 9 to 10 P.M. They refused, however, to give him a regular allowance. Harold seemed unable to accept any of the worker's suggestions for modifying his behavior, and responded to any such discussion by further acting out. The clinic then decided to recommend placement in an institution and assumed responsibility for working out placement plans. The six months of treatment had been effective only to the extent that both Harold and his parents were willing to consider and to follow through on placement for Harold in a cottage type of institution.

49

Selection of Techniques

The tempo of the treatment process with delinquents presents great variations. In some instances a relatively long period is required to establish a meaningful relationship with them. Our experience at the clinic indicated that a relationship tended to develop slowly and precariously, particularly with individuals who had severe conduct disorders or character neuroses with prominent psychopathic traits. We did not find that such slowness in forming relationships necessarily operated with delinquent adolescents who fell into other categories. As clinicians in any setting can testify, however, the variations within any diagnostic category are infinite. It seems important to stress the need for specificity in approach, because of the widespread tendency to regard delinquents as a categorical group and to generalize about such matters as timing, level, and pace of treatment.

In the early stages of treatment with the neurotic or non-psychopathic delinquent child, the worker must show active interest and be non-judgmental and selectively partisan. He must be as wary about making direct interpretations as he would be in any therapeutic relationship. Our experience tallies with that of other social workers, psychoanalysts, and psychiatrists who have been aware that the path to the adolescent's inner problem often can be traversed only if one is willing to endeavor to modify some of the external pressures with which the adolescent is unable to cope. An illustration of this dual approach follows.

IRMA K

Irma was 13 years old when she was brought into court by the Society for the Prevention of Cruelty to Children, after she had attempted to commit suicide by drinking iodine. The agency's report stated that the girl said she had made a suicide attempt because of her guilt about having had sexual intercourse with two boys during the previous month. The diagnostic examination disclosed that Irma's intelligence was within normal range (I.Q. 110) but that, because of her disturbance at the time of the examination, she perhaps was not functioning at the level of her potential capacity. The psychiatrist, in his report, described her as hyperactive in the interview. She was a nail biter, had a slight stutter, and had a history of continued nightmares for several years. Her disturbance was diagnosed as a conduct disorder with neurotic traits.

Irma was the second in a family of four children. Her father, a chronic alcoholic, had deserted the family about six months before Irma's suicidal attempt. Her mother, a rigid and punitive woman, had little warmth or affection for any of her children and was overtly hostile toward Irma. Irma had an older brother, 16, and two younger sisters of 12 and 10. The family had been living on a department of welfare allowance since Irma's birth.

During the intake interview, Irma responded quickly to an offer of help. She spontaneously told the worker that one of her main troubles was that she hated school. She had been transferred to her present school immediately after her father had deserted. She said her mother felt she could not continue to give her carfare as she had done previously. She was now attending a school within walking distance of her home; no one there helped her and she hated everyone. The intake worker offered to talk with the principal and teachers to see what might be done, and Irma responded positively to this suggestion.

When the worker visited the school, she found that the principal and the teacher were severely critical of Irma because of some minor insubordinations in the classroom. For some reason Irma had been placed in a class for children with lower than normal intelligence. Irma, however, was failing in all subjects. When the worker pointed out that Irma had skipped two grades and had been on the honor roll consistently in her former school, the principal became concerned and offered to look into the matter. Subsequently Irma's program was changed and the school personnel made a real effort to give her special attention and recognition. Irma's provocative behavior in the classroom disappeared and by the end of the year she was again getting honor grades.

She kept her appointments at the clinic and used the relationship with the worker to discuss some of her problems with her siblings and her parents. She began to associate with a pre-adolescent group in the community, which gave her considerable pleasure. Her relationship with boys her own age began to follow

51

the usual adolescent pattern. She stopped biting her nails, her stuttering diminished considerably, and she was no longer troubled by nightmares. Her mother had refused to have regular contact with the clinic worker but her pressures on Irma relaxed as Irma's behavior improved.

Although treatment was focused on Irma's reality situation, it was integrally related to the girl's psychodynamics. It was apparent from the history that Irma's success at school had been her chief source of security. The unhappy shift to a new school, following her father's desertion and her mother's increased hostility, stripped her of her last remnant of security and status, and thus precipitated her into sexual activities. The suicide attempt, which undoubtedly contained elements of deep guilt and aggression, also represented an expression of her rage at her current deprivations and frustrations. When her school situation improved and she felt the interest of the principal, her teacher, and the worker, she was able to respond positively, both in school and in the treatment situation. In the treatment interviews, she was given some help with her feelings of guilt and, with the support of the worker, she was able to seek more social satisfactions.

Reactions to Increased Anxiety

During the treatment experience, most delinquent youngsters have periods of intensified guilt and anxiety, not only when painful material comes to the fore, but also when real dangers impinge upon them from the outside. Such threats, both inner and outer, bring with them increased tension and a resurgence of resistance which often are expressed in renewed delinquencies. Just as the non-delinquent neurotic during a period of increased tension may have a recurrence of somatic or affective symptoms, so the delinquent, who uses his acting out as a release valve for his tension, may engage in renewed delinquent acts. The delinquent unconsciously utilizes the outlet that he previously had found effective; in his acting-out behavior, he also attempts, by precipitating another court appearance, to terminate treatment.

At this juncture in treatment, the therapist's course must be guided by diagnostic considerations. If the adolescent's superego is reasonably strong, the therapist may attempt to help him see the connections between his delinquency and the provocation; the therapist should be aware, however, that this technique engenders even greater anxiety and is therefore useless, and possibly dangerous, if the relationship is not on a firm footing. When this treatment maneuver succeeds in curbing or reducing the delinquent acts, the adolescent's guilt and anxiety again come to the fore. Treatment for him then closely parallels that for other anxious, frustrated, or emotionally immature young people.

When a phase of increased tension appears in the course of treatment of adolescents whose disturbances fall into the general group of character disorders, they are likely to become too anxious to remain in treatment. If the tensions are largely the result of external difficulties, supportive measures are usually indicated. If the threat, however, is largely an internal one, that is, fear of losing gratifications because of growing attachment to the therapist, the adolescent may not be able to tolerate a close treatment relationship. Sometimes an authoritative relationship with a probation officer or staff members of an institution is all that the adolescent can tolerate at this phase of his development.

IRVING B

Irving was first brought to court at the age of 11 for stealing jewelry and money. At 13 he was brought to court again, this time for stealing a bicycle. He was referred for psychiatric examination.

The report of the diagnostic study described Irving as restless and troubled, with great inner stresses. He seemed unsure of himself and had a limited view of his own capacities. He had scored an I.Q. of 104, but he seemed to have a higher potential. Irving was referred to the clinic for treatment on the basis of his expressed guilt feelings and seeming ability to enter into a relationship.

The B family consisted of Irving's mother, an immature woman, whose relationship to Irving was ambivalent, at times openly seductive and at others severely rejecting; a stepfather who was interested in Irving although blocked from effectual contact with him by Mrs. B; a stepbrother 7 years old with whom he was in open competition.

53

The treatment process from the very beginning was punctuated with repeated delinquencies. Before the end of the second month of treatment Irving was brought into court for stealing a car. In his interviews at the time he exhibited great anxiety about his relationship with his mother; he appeared to be trying to make some identification with his stepfather but the mother prevented this by using the stepfather as a means to punish Irving for his misbehavior. Irving also brought out, with progressively less inhibition, hostility toward his young and openly-favored brother.

After six months of treatment, during which Irving kept his appointments regularly, his overt symptoms of anxiety seemed to increase. He developed a tic—blinking of the eyes—and complained of severe nightmares and diffuse fears. At the same time he continued to get into increasingly serious difficulty in the community. He seemed actually to be driven to commit acts that end in commitment to an institution. It seemed best, therefore, to return the case to court and arrange to have Irving assigned to the supervision of a probation officer.

Use of Play Techniques

At the clinic a number of younger children, especially those in the 8- to 10-year age range, were treated through play techniques, rather than through the medium of verbal interviews. Play materials were also found to have some usefulness in our work with pre-adolescents and adolescents.

The use of "play" with delinquent children, however, presents some special problems. To invite a child who has just recently gone through a frightening court hearing to play out his fantasies, which are likely to have highly destructive or aggressive content, is obviously unwise. Unless a child is truly split off from reality, entering into such play sharpens his conflict and increases his anxiety. He knows that he is at the clinic because he cannot acceptably handle his drives in relation to society. If he is encouraged through play to give free rein to his impulses and to set aside his defenses, he is likely to be overwhelmed with anxiety. Also he knows that if his defenses are further weakened he is in danger of repeating the behavior.

54

The clinic records are replete with statements that initially children played cautiously, with the finger paints, plasticine dolls, or toys. As they gained security with the worker, they seemed to use the materials with greater freedom and pleasure. Even more than other children, the young delinquent must be helped to strengthen his healthy defenses to handle his drives. He must, in effect, be given the usual support needed by children, plus protection against further acting out.

Because the majority of children coming to the clinic are adolescents, the use of play has been rather limited. The kind of pathology—social, emotional, or intellectual—will of course determine whether some use of play is advisable and also the choice of play materials. Plasticine, finger paints, water, dolls, doll furniture, blocks, building and sewing materials, model planes, wagons, competitive games like checkers and cards, toy guns and knives, are all available and are put to various uses.

The techniques of play therapy obviously cannot be discussed here. At the clinic, an effort was made to utilize play as a therapeutic activity in various ways and for varying treatment ends. Sometimes play was used as an escape from the intensity of the treatment situation, or as a peripheral, rather than a central, treatment method.

One example of play as an escape is the "horseplay" that the adolescent boys engage in during their group sessions.[2] Some roughhouse activity as well as card playing and the reading of comic books are engaged in frequently in the therapy groups. These activities are often the vehicles for the covert expression of resistance or other feelings and, as such, must be understood and appropriately handled by the therapist. They are most likely to take place when the discussion arouses intense feeling and discomfort in the adolescents. Sometimes it is important that the meaning of the activity should be commented on or interpreted by the therapist or one of the members of the group. At other times, especially when the tension is particularly great, it may be advisable to permit the activity to continue unmarked by any comment.

[2] See William C, p. 75.

Treatment of Parents

Any sound evaluation of an adolescent's treatment requirements or therapeutic potential must take into account the influence of significant persons in his family and the nature of his social and group relationships. Similarly, the picture of the delinquent's family is not complete if an examination of its place in the socioeconomic and cultural life of the community is omitted.

It has been noted by persons who have worked with delinquents that sometimes a parent of a delinquent—or in fact the family unit itself—maintains an equilibrium, precarious as it may be, by the very fact that a child engages in delinquent activities. Our experience at the clinic confirms this observation. In such families the delinquent adolescent seems to be subjected to greater provocation from members of his family when his behavior improves. Because these family members, usually the parents, gain some sort of gratification from the child's delinquent behavior, it is highly important that they too have an opportunity to redirect their drives. To put it another way, an important function of the clinic or social agency is to give the parents an opportunity to work out their conflicts directly, through treatment, rather than indirectly, through stimulating further delinquent activities by their children.

In order to establish a treatment relationship with these parents, the role of the agency must be explained again and again. The worker obviously cannot abet them in their wish to use the agency, and through it the court, to gain punishment or leniency for the child. Clarifying the therapeutic function itself often precipitates in these parents responses that open the way to discussion of their feelings toward authority and their difficult experiences with their own parents. Often, when these parents come to understand that the permissive attitudes of the worker are likely to connote that he is not in agreement with their demands for punishment of their child, they endeavor to withdraw from contact. Whether a parent can be involved in treatment depends on many factors, chief among which are the extent of his positive interest and the depth of his involvement in the child's welfare. Such positive factors are often present in even the most outwardly rejecting parent.

In the course of treatment, an examination of these very acts of rejection often generates guilt and anxiety that can be mobilized constructively. The establishment of relationship is facilitated if the worker can accept such acts for what they often are—reflections of the parent's desperate struggle to maintain an equilibrium against overwhelming pressure. In the course of a therapeutic relationship, some parents are enabled to modify certain basic attitudes. In other instances, they develop sufficient identification with the worker to take over some of his attitudes toward their children. In either event, the treatment may succeed in stabilizing the family, and these changes, even though temporary, often make it possible for the adolescent to consolidate the gains he has made in his own treatment. Sometimes permanent improvement accrues, since the neurotic cycle has been broken.

The most perplexing problem in the treatment of the parents of delinquents, after the initial resistance has been at least partially resolved, is that of focus. Basically, the parent is drawn into treatment because of the part he plays in creating his child's difficulties. A "plus" factor in these cases, however, is that the parent, because of the child's court experience, has become involved with a social agency almost against his will. His resistance, therefore, at any point in treatment, must be viewed in the context of his forced involvement. The non-judgmental, non-punitive attitude of the worker may arouse a great deal of guilt and anxiety in the neurotic parent, giving rise to strong resistance. The resistance is likely to become insuperable if the worker does not recognize and handle anxiety on various levels—in relation to the client's own problems, to his guilt about his treatment of his child, and to his continuing resentment at being involved with the agency. To handle the parent's resistance effectively requires discussion of current feelings about his continuing contact with the agency as well as of his feelings and attitudes about his life experiences and relationships.

The whole complex of the economic and social forces that operate to make delinquency more prevalent in deprived areas than in better neighborhoods affects the content of discussion with parents of delinquents and often the goal and direction of treatment. The importance of becoming aware of the reality factors in their lives cannot be overstressed. The pressures in their daily existence are often so great that channels for constructive activity,. sublimation, and release of tension are extremely limited. These parents often literally spend their lives within the four walls of a tenement flat. They may have unsatisfied basic needs for food,. clothing, and shelter, as well as for education, recreation, medical service, counseling, and guidance.

The treatment hour often proceeds with an undercurrent of pressure because of the encroachment on the parents' time—time to make the trip to the agency as well as for the actual interview itself. Often they lose several hours of work from a badly needed job or they leave the children at home uncared for and multiple household chores undone. Also, to many of the parents the experience of spending time with an interested adult to discuss their needs and problems is an entirely new one to which, in the beginning, they are not able to attach much importance. Obviously, some parents use the reality difficulties to avoid contact. The nature of the pressures, however, must be carefully evaluated before the parents' reluctance to keep appointments can be ascribed to resistance. Certainly the reality demands, as well as a parent's psychological drives, must be appraised in order to understand the negative responses to treatment and to offers of help for himself or his child. The fact that this offer is made by a worker who represents the court, however indirectly, does not make acceptance of help any easier. The parents inevitably identify the worker with their concept—derived from real experiences or fantasies—of an authoritative figure.

Planning for Institutional Care

Because of the variety of disturbances found among delinquents,. the social worker attached to a court clinic must frequently utilize institutional resources to further both diagnosis and treatment. Arranging for a period of observation in a psychiatric hospital or for admission to mental hospitals, schools for mental defectives,. or other special treatment facilities is a recurrent responsibility. Even when an adolescent is manifestly psychotic or mentally defective, the task of preparing him and his family for his placement is far from simple. Often both the parent and adolescent may need a period of intensive help if they are to utilize the facility constructively.

Certain other disturbed adolescents also frequently need some sort of custodial care. At the clinic we have endeavored to work out placement plans with them and their parents. Some of these adolescents needed placement because their total situation was so lacking in emotional and social satisfactions and in growth opportunities that adjustment at home was deemed impossible. Treatment in an intramural setting also seemed indicated for a group of adolescents who had previously been accepted for therapy and had made some gains but who, nonetheless, continued to act out in an antisocial manner which was dangerous both to them and to the community. A small number were children accepted for a period of treatment with the goal of placement in view from the outset.

The adolescent in need of placement has usually experienced intense rejection from his family, either because of his own personality difficulties or because of the disturbances of other members of his family; typically, of course, it is the result of the interaction of negative factors in the parent-child relationship. The child responds to rejection by his family with anxiety and hostility; these feelings may be expressed in overt hostile acts, or they may take the form of destructive fantasies that must usually be rigorously repressed. The delinquent who is about to be placed away from home, therefore, is often extremely anxious. Placement appears to him to be not only a punishment for his delinquencies but also a reprisal for his destructive thoughts and fantasies; in consequence it confirms his most distorted and exaggerated feelings of guilt and self-blame. For most of these young people, placement represents a final act of parental punishment and rejection.

It is not surprising, therefore, that during the period in which placement is being planned, an adolescent manifests an increase in anxiety, guilt, and hostility and frequently repeats, sometimes in an even more severe form, his earlier delinquent activities. In work with delinquents, it is axiomatic that placement as a remedy exacerbates the symptoms. This is true even when a suitable

59

facility is available. When the facility is anything but desirable, which is frequently the case, placement may be a permanently damaging experience.

The parent of an adolescent who is to be placed also goes through considerable emotional upheaval. He, too, is frequently ridden by feelings of guilt and anxiety. To him placement is often tantamount to admitting that he has failed as a parent. Such an admission carries with it considerable pain, particularly in a culture such as ours which places primary responsibility for child care and child rearing on the parents. When placement of the child is under consideration, the parent is likely, because of his overwhelming sense of guilt, to project and displace blame onto others—with the adolescent himself serving as the most convenient target. Since the adolescent usually has committed serious delinquent acts, the parent in reality has a detailed list of his child's misdeeds at his fingertips. Even parents who have been overprotective, and who previously have attempted to conceal the difficulties of their child, often begin to emphasize his bad points and exaggerate his misbehavior, in an effort to relieve their own feelings of guilt about the placement. During the period when placement plans are being implemented, it is not unusual for a parent to provoke his child, almost deliberately, into new delinquencies in order to justify the placement plan.

Not only the delinquent, but other members of the family, become the recipient of the parent's projections of blame during the placement process. Frequently the parents blame and attack each other. Even before the question of placement has arisen, most of these parents have had varying degrees of marital conflict. Delinquency, as we know, has a high correlation with parental discord and family disruptions. A consideration of placement plans, therefore, far from tending to resolve such marital conflicts, frequently intensifies them and, at the same time, results in increased provocation by both parents of the adolescent. These attacks on the child and on each other are not merely reactions to the placement; these tactics are often utilized to conceal other conflicts that are too threatening and anxiety-laden to be faced openly. The child who is placed, therefore, often carries with him, as a parting gift from his parents, the burden of their displaced guilt. The ado-

60

lescent himself, unfortunately, is not aware that their guilt stems from events that may have taken place long before his birth. His own inner guilt, however, impels him to take over only too readily this heavy and unjust burden.

For both child and parent, the reality of separation, which itself is painful, is made more unbearable by the accumulation of tension and the accretion of guilt. During the period of implementing placement plans, the problems of managing treatment are particularly difficult. Treatment goals must be feasible in relation to the time available to achieve them. Judicious limits must be set on catharsis and anxiety-provoking revelations. Strong supportive techniques are often required, with the aim of reinforcing the positive feelings of parent and child toward each other.

Unfortunately, working with a family on a placement plan for a delinquent child is further complicated by the fact that the facilities for care are usually unalluring and often grim. Because of his antisocial behavior and also because of entrenched community attitudes, the child who has passed through the courts usually must be placed in an institution for "delinquents." Most other child care institutions accept only "neglected and dependent" children. In the light of modern psychiatric knowledge, endeavoring to make this distinction becomes a form of hair-splitting. As an added problem, facilities for the care of all categories of children are inadequate. The institutions for dependent and neglected children are overcrowded and under-staffed; this is also almost universally true of the much smaller number of institutions for delinquents.

As part of its total treatment program, the clinic assumed responsibility for working through plans for children to be placed. We therefore undertook to prepare the child and his parents for placement and to confer with the institutional personnel. In these conferences, the clinic worker presented the clinic's findings and, in consultation with the staff, worked out procedures that might ease the experience for the child. During this painful period of change the clinic worker was often the only constant element in the child's life. The value of the relationship at this time was brought out clearly many times in the adolescent's early letters from the institution to his worker and also in the worker's occasional contacts with the child at the institution.[3] The continuity of contact during the placement procedures obviously is of equal importance in settings other than the clinic.

Carrying out these placement procedures for delinquent children is extremely time-consuming. The question inevitably arises as to whether this treatment responsibility could not be carried more effectively by a child-placing facility itself, rather than by the children's court, the clinic, or the social agency where such cases originate. Certainly the delinquent adolescents are in need of skilful help and careful planning if they are not to travel the road from institutions for delinquents to reformatories and state prisons. In actual practice, delinquent children are treated as second- or third-rate citizens when they must be removed from their own homes. Foster homes are almost completely unavailable for this group. The special institutions for the delinquent rarely offer specialized treatment. In the main, the delinquent is given only custodial care, largely for the purpose of protecting the community from his misdeeds. If treatment facilities in the institution are available at all, they are generally inadequate.

The clinic's plan for carrying responsibility for initial placement of a few children is obviously a palliative measure. It is in no sense proposed as a solution to a long neglected problem of providing adequate facilities and treatment services for these deprived and disturbed youngsters. The responsibility for providing such essential services rests with the whole community.

[3] The clinic does only a limited type of follow up with children who have been institutionalized. The court usually drops contact except in instances where the institution is unwilling or unable to keep the child.

V. Group Therapy for Adolescents

GROUP PSYCHOTHERAPY CURRENTLY is being added to the traditional treatment methods by many clinics and social agencies. Although it often is still considered something of an experimental luxury, evidence of its value is steadily accumulating. Some agencies may seize on group therapy as a device for saving staff time and discover later that it proves to have an opposite effect. Viewed realistically, it is an additional or supplementary service that actually places greater burdens on the professional staff. Agencies that work with delinquent adolescents have initiated group treatment largely in an attempt to reach certain individuals who seem unable to profit by individual treatment. The failure of individual treatment for these delinquents is often the equivalent of a sentence of doom, since most of them have had a try at many other available community resources. Since the court action is often used as a last resort, the adolescents who reach the court clinic are often the most refractory cases. They frequently elude the clinic, and their referral to another resource is usually only a perfunctory gesture.

The initial work with group therapy at the court clinic was begun in 1947. This program was undertaken in the hope that it would provide a means of helping those for whom there otherwise would be no help at all. During the first two years, we accepted in our groups only adolescents or their parents whom we had failed to reach through individual therapy. The purpose of this restriction was to help us assess the contributions of group therapy to the treatment of these individuals. Cases were accepted for group therapy if, after a period of six months to a year of individual treatment, there appeared to be no progress at all or there was evidence of actual deterioration in the clients. Among the adolescents accepted, many were failing to keep their appointments or kept them only sporadically. Practically all of them had failed to establish even a minimal relationship with a therapist. They were either uncommunicative in their interviews or obviously evaded any kind of discussion or experience with the therapist which would involve them emotionally. A number of these adolescents were continuing to engage in serious delinquency, and placement seemed to be the only recourse for many of them.

The parents included in our first groups were ones who were sabotaging, in one way or another, the treatment of their children. Sometimes they seemed actually to be worsening the child's reality situation, in spite of the fact that he was apparently making progress. Other parents appeared to be provoking the child into further delinquency. Some parents had crucial personal problems which, although directly related to the adolescent's difficulties, could not be examined because of their seemingly impenetrable resistance.

The hope that group therapy might provide some help for these elusive and difficult adolescents and parents was based on the recognition that many of them, in spite of their poor relationships with their therapists, were able to enter into relationships with other people from which they derived some satisfaction. Since group therapy depends largely on interactions between the members of the group, it seemed possible that productive results might be achieved by bringing a number of these individuals together in carefully planned combinations.

The rapidly growing literature on group therapy gave us some base for our optimism. The rationale, as described by one of the authors of this volume, is as follows:

64

The patients in groups seem to have therapeutically significant relationships between themselves in addition to the shadowy reflection of parental or sibling conflicts; for even at the outset, one can detect the ties which represent the reality of the patient's present social relationships. These ties may assume the form of common problems, similar family or work experiences, or central cultural interests. In ordinary social relationships on meeting a stranger we often find ourselves trying to dig up a mutual acquaintance or a common past experience. Slavson speaks of "social hunger"; but whatever we call these manifestations they seem to grow out of the essential nature of man as an organism operating within a society in which his very existence depends upon the co-operative labor of his fellows.

Within the therapy group some patients quickly proceed to establish and utilize these co-operative ties. Others distort or deny them and a few may seek to establish such ties where none really exist. However, in the therapy group we have access to these distortions very much as they occur in the patient's day-to-day relationships. For although the historical beginnings of such distortions may be traceable to early family life, they have been shaped and maintained by later life experiences which may contain elements similar to those in the earlier situations. This similarity is not simply a figment of the patient's distortions but often reflects the presence of those destructive forces in our society which act on family, work, and social life alike.

The patient may thus come to invest a mate, friend, or fellow worker with values inappropriate to the actual nature of their true social relationship to him. For example, a patient may react to prolonged and continuous threats to his security with the generalization that most people are only waiting to attack or get the better of him, and he may then elaborate certain exploitative devices of his own designed to protect him. On the other hand his defense against hurt may be to evade the brutal competitive struggle he feels life to be, and he may employ elaborate camouflage to deny to himself qualities in people or situations which may conflict with his own picture of himself. Characteristically he fails to perceive or utilize the common or co-operative elements existing between himself and others who have such basic ties to him as those of class, real goals, or mutual problems.

The patient's basic distortions may be most apparent in his relationships to certain types of people as for example the opposite sex or dominating, authoritative figures. On the other hand he may be able to set up more adequate and satisfying relationships with the same sex or with more submissive individuals.

A properly selected group will thus expose the patient's characteristic distortions as they appear in the interaction between himself and certain members of the group. Since he is also capable of entering into relatively healthy relationships with certain other members of the group he is able more easily to examine and work through his relationship distortions because he is supported by the reassuring reality of his healthy social ties within the group.[1]

---

[1] Harris B. Peck, M.D., "Group Psychotherapy and Mental Health," *International Journal of Group Psychotherapy*, Vol. I, No. 4 (1951), pp. 303–305.

General Techniques

Almost all the adolescents referred for our therapy groups because of failure in individual treatment were accepted. We endeavored, so far as possible, to place them in a group that seemed most likely to meet their needs in accordance with principles of grouping. The first groups were conducted for adolescents between 14 and 16, the age range that represents the heaviest concentration of cases for both the court and the clinic, as well as the highest incidence of treatment failures. We included, however, several children who were as young as $12\frac{1}{2}$ and a few who had passed their 17th birthday.

The size of groups at the clinic usually did not exceed eight clients and was usually around five or six. Sessions were held once a week and were about an hour and a half in length. When possible, groups were conducted on a continuing basis, with some new members coming in and others leaving from time to time. The rooms used for the group sessions were usually the offices of the staff members. Seating arrangements were informal; the circular or semicircular arrangement of the chairs with the therapist a part of the circle was the one most frequently used. Refreshments were usually served during the meeting and about every sixth meeting most groups would go on some kind of outing to a gymnasium, a swimming pool, or a movie.

Our early sessions were held in a room equipped with a one-way screen and observation booth. In selected sessions, a tape recording machine was also used. These devices and their purpose were discussed frankly with the group members and their questions and negative reactions were worked through in so far as possible. The question of records was discussed in much the same way as in individual treatment. The confidentiality of personal material and the relationship of the therapist to the court were explained. The attitudes about records were recognized as a problem related to treatment, but due consideration was given to the reality elements that might have contributed to the clients' suspiciousness and mistrust. Explanations about the clinic's interest in research were presented, although we realized that they would not be fully accepted or even entirely understood. We found, in comparing groups where the one-way screen or sound recordings were used and those where they were not, the differences in reaction were most marked in the early sessions. The use of these devices appeared to increase the group's caution, which was manifest in the less frequent discussion of material pertaining to violations of probation and sexual fantasies, and in less use of profanity. Such caution, however, tended to disappear after two or three months; the group then practically ignored both the screen and the recording machine. Nevertheless, there can be no doubt that their use did sometimes influence the course of the sessions in which they were employed. It seemed undesirable, however, to employ concealed recording devices, and the recording procedures that were employed seemed justified from a research point of view, since comparable data could not be obtained in any other way. These verbatim records, which we endeavored to keep during the first three or four years of our programs, were utilized for research and teaching purposes. Currently most group therapists dictate immediately after a session; no recording devices or observers are used except for special projects.

The adolescents selected for the group sessions had a variety of disturbances. The clinical syndromes included early or latent schizophrenia, psychopathy, and acute neurosis; most of the adolescents, however, were found to have severe conduct disorders or long-standing, chronic neurotic illnesses resulting primarily in disturbances in character. Both of these last two groupings usually manifested behavior which was psychopathic in nature but which did not seem, on the basis of history, clinical observation, and psychological testing, to be true psychopathy.[2]

The groups, in general, were so constituted that no more than two of the members manifested extreme psychopathic trends. Also an effort was made to include one or two members whose superego structure was more or less intact and in whom guilt and anxiety were easily mobilized. The balance of the membership fell somewhere between these two poles. In the beginning we were concerned about the risk of overloading the group with withdrawn or passive individuals since many of the children suggested for group treatment appeared to be of this type. It soon became apparent,

[2] See Chapter I, Patterns of Pathology, pp. 5–18.

however, that a number of the children who had appeared passive in individual sessions rapidly became surprisingly active in the group setting. The staff subsequently learned to gauge the potentials of group participation more accurately.

As noted earlier, the children selected for the first therapy groups had shown a high degree of resistance to individual treatment. The amount of difficulty which had been encountered in working through these resistances depended upon many and varied factors including the fixity, severity, and duration of the pathology as well as the skill of the worker. It was the impression of the staff that the problems presented by these children were "tough ones"; that is, that these children had severe and crystallized pathology, high resistances, strongly mobilized defenses, and generally poor prognoses.

The clinic workers, in treating them, had been faced with a paradox familiar to all who have worked with delinquents. These children reached the court because of certain characteristic disturbances in their relations with authority which made it practically impossible to treat them in any other setting; yet the court experience, in itself, seemed to intensify their previously formed patterns of defense to such a degree as to create an insurmountable resistance to treatment. Resistance, of course, may serve as the worker's first therapeutic foothold. But before it can be utilized as a means of involving the patient, it must first be correctly diagnosed and understood by the therapist and made apparent to the patient through the medium of the relationship. With these adolescents selected for group therapy it had not been possible, after many months in individual treatment, to bring the resistance into the open and to externalize it. Within the first few group sessions, however, characteristic aspects of resistance were quickly externalized and expressed with considerable directness. Although this was very encouraging, it was sometimes difficult to direct.[3]

[3] The clinic's follow-up studies of its early therapy groups indicate that, of all adolescents placed in groups after failure in individual treatment, about 60 per cent achieved varying degrees of improvement. In such pilot evaluations, however, made only a few years after the completion of treatment, the results must be viewed critically. The work of the Gluecks suggests that apparent progress in a delinquent may be but superficial alteration of overt patterns.

A summary, with some verbatim recording of one case, may help to show how resistance is brought to the fore in a group setting and how the therapist and the group aid the delinquent in facing his problems.

MARTIN L

Martin was 16 years old when he was brought into court by his father. In the complaint his parents stated that he was uncontrollable at home, was truanting from school, and had been stealing. The court referred him to the clinic for diagnostic study. The diagnosis made was that of severe character neurosis with strong psychopathic elements. It was recommended that the judge refer him to the clinic for treatment. Martin was one of ten children. His mother seemed hostile and rejecting of him, and the father passively acquiescent. The mother worked sporadically; the father had been ill and unemployed for some years. Little was known about Martin's relationship with his siblings. When Martin came to the clinic he said he had been told that he could not graduate from high school because of his truanting, although he was in his last term.

Martin was extremely skeptical about getting any help from the clinic worker. He had run away twice during the interval between the diagnostic examination and the intake interview, and he threatened to run away again, to steal, or to get into other trouble. The intake worker felt, however, that Martin's situation was so desperate that some attempt ought to be made to try to reach him.

During a period of seven months, Martin kept his appointments only sporadically. He was guarded and evasive, and resisted every approach that threatened his defenses. At no time did he display any hostility or negative feelings about treatment or about his therapist, continuing to be amiable. He reported that he was conforming at home and in the community, although he actually was engaged in many delinquencies. The home situation seemed to be intensifying Martin's difficulties and attempts were made by the clinic to involve the parents in treatment. This effort, too, was unsuccessful. Placement seemed the only alternative but Martin would not tolerate any mention of it. Also, the use of coercive measures to accomplish it would probably have doomed the experience to failure before it had even begun. The decision to try Martin in a therapy group was made without any real expectation of positive results.

In the first session of a newly formed group, Martin was the most outspokenly distrustful and hostile member. He was particularly suspicious of the sound-recording apparatus and inquired directly about the use to which the records might be put. He had an air of frank disgust with the entire proceedings. He intimated that he was "wise" to all these dubious machinations and wished only that the therapist would hurry up and get through with whatever he had to say. He seemed to be thrown a little off balance by the therapist's relative silence. Almost in spite of himself, Martin was drawn into a discussion when the group members began talking about their encounters with the police. It was at this point that he began to give some intimation of the experiences that had made him so guarded, suspicious, and evasive. The boys exchanged stories about their stays at various institutions and Martin fell in by bragging about some of the dangerous situations in which he had been involved.

In the brief excerpt that follows it is possible to catch a glimpse of the rapid way in which common ground was established between Martin and certain other boys in the group. This made possible the kind of identification that had been so difficult for Martin to achieve with even a most understanding and sympathetic worker, in individual treatment.

Therapy Group Experience

MARTIN: A cop once took three shots at me. . . . I was just walking down the street minding my own business.

Harold: They do that because they are scared of us.

MARTIN: One time I was on the roof and they came up after me. Me and another fellow lay down so they wouldn't see us. I went down the fire escape and then some lady yelled out and they began firing shots through the window. I dropped down onto the grass and started running but they followed us.

Leonard: Did they try to kill you?

MARTIN: I didn't stay there to see what happened.

Harold: Once a cop took a shot at me and he really wanted to kill me. . . .

MARTIN: You know what happened to me only last night? We were standing around on the corner fooling around with a couple of girls and a cop came over and told us to go home. We didn't feel like going home because it was too early so we just went around the other way and the cop stopped us again. He tried to make me move so I just walked away but I was so mad I went to the drug store and called up the precinct and started to give them a piece of my mind. Then I beat it and the cops were looking for us all night. *(The entire group roars with laughter.)*

Ronald *(angrily)*: For crying out loud, just for standing around on a corner.

Martin: Yeah, I wouldn't mind if they chased us away if we were hollering or raising a fuss or something.

Here several of the other boys joined in and told of similar experiences with the police in which they felt they had been treated unjustly. One boy told of brutal beatings he said were given to him without cause. Another told of having his money taken away by a detective who later in court denied that he had done so. At this point Martin seemed suddenly to reverse direction in a most surprising way and began to talk of quite a different sort of experience at the hands of an authority.

Martin: Do you know who is a swell cop? *(He mentions the name of a policeman who is apparently known to several of the other boys.)*

Leonard: Yeah, that's the kind of cops they should have, one who understands you.

Martin: You know what he did one time? There was a Spanish guy who was giving him a hard time and the Spanish guy said to him, "Why if you didn't have that club, I would wipe the street up with you." This cop just took off his coat and his badge and he had a fair fight with the guy. The guy did wipe the street up with him too.

This interchange seemed to encourage the other boys to talk about more positive experiences with authority. They spoke of the fair treatment they had at the detention home and indicated that certain staff members at the clinic seemed to treat them pretty decently too. One of the boys, Burt, said that this was the sort of treatment that should be accorded them in the police station.

Burt: You know what they should have? Something like a counselor from the clinic right in the police station so that when you go there he would listen while the detective was talking to you and if he slapped you around or something like that the counselor would be right there to protect you. . . .

Martin *(vehemently)*: That idea of having a counselor in the precinct. . . . I don't like that at all.

Therapist: You don't think much of that idea?

Martin: I'll tell you something about that. If I was going to rob a store

71

I would figure on what's going to happen to me if I get caught. As it is now if I get caught I will be taken to a police station and I am damn sure that when I get there I will get a shellacking, and that's what makes a guy get a little nervous and that is a good thing.

Therapist: What do the rest of you think about that?

Mitchell: Sure, if I was going to rob a store I would figure if I got caught I wouldn't have anything to worry about because there would be a counselor there and I wouldn't get hit.

MARTIN: That's exactly right. . . . Sure, I mean I would go and pull a job on a store if I knew they would go easy on me. After all, if they put me in the detention home I get fed and everything. Sometimes maybe I couldn't even get treated that good on the outside.

Later in this session Martin talked of the various institutions to which he might be sent but from which he was sure he could escape. The group reminded him that it was even easier to "break out" of the clinic. After hesitating a moment he mumbled, "Well, maybe I just don't want to."

Martin here revealed a significant clue to the pattern of his frequent "escapes" which invariably ended either in his easy capture or in his giving himself up. We see his strong drive toward punishment. We also gain a momentary glimpse of his guilt, anxiety, and fear of losing control which gave rise to his need to see all authority as rigid and punitive. The group situation doubtless was disturbing to Martin since it did not conform to his requirements of authority. Although it set some limits, it was neither rigid nor punitive and such a relatively permissive setting would stimulate his anxiety. Despite its dangerous nature, the group experience must also have held out some promise of a solution to his problems.

At the next session, Martin appeared a half hour late, accompanied by a friend. He made a dramatic entrance and announced that he had remained out late one night during the week and now had not been home for several days. He said he did not see how he could return home or go back to school again.

Therapist: Well, what do you want to do?

MARTIN: I don't know. That's what I came here to find out.

During the session Martin used the group for precisely this purpose. The group discussed his problem at length and decided, in view of the fact that he had only two more weeks of school until graduation, that it might be best for him to remain at home at least until then. After much discussion about the difficulties

72

involved in such a plan, Martin agreed to try to carry it out. He did so successfully and was graduated with his class. During the next three months, Martin attended group sessions regularly and discussed some of his feeling of inadequacy as evidenced by his failure to obtain a job, and his fury at the "riding" he received at the hands of his family. At one point he became discouraged and, for the first time, missed three sessions in a row.

When we next heard of him, he was in the detention home on a charge of having stolen a car for a "joy ride." He spontaneously asked the detention home authorities for permission to attend the group sessions, which was granted. On his return to the group, Martin frankly stated that he had tried to "make a go of it" but that he knew that he couldn't control himself. He said it was impossible for him to stay out of trouble while he remained at home and the group agreed with him. They discussed a plan he proposed of going to live with some friends in an upstate community. The therapist suggested that Martin explore this possibility. When Martin returned the next week, it was he himself who recognized that the plan was not feasible. He and the group then decided that for the present there was no alternative but to go to the state training school. He faced this decision realistically. He examined the undesirable aspects of institutional placement but resolved, nevertheless, to go through with it. He did so, and the therapist continued to hear from him. He made an excellent adjustment in the institution where he remained for over eighteen months. Following his discharge, he returned to his family and secured a job on which he did well. About a year later he moved out of his home. There have been no further arrests or complaints.

The group therapy experience obviously did not "cure" Martin's neurosis. It succeeded, however, in drastically altering, at a critical point in the boy's life, the way he related to authority. Institutionalization would probably have been a wholly destructive experience if this change in feeling had not been effected. Coercive procedures would only have confirmed his own distorted ideas about the world in general and about authority in particular. He doubtless was better able to accept a solution arrived at by the group than any that might have been evolved in individual treatment, not only because it seemed less arbitrary but because it grew out of a vital process that went on between him and his contemporaries. The way in which group identification helped solve this boy's problem is not too different from the process that normally operates when an adolescent makes a transition from the standards of parental figures to the mores, laws, and customs of his contemporaries.[4] In Martin's case, this incorporation of group mores was made possible by a specially constructed group in an authoritative setting.

Martin's problem is typical of those of many delinquent adolescents who require placement. Because of the value of the group process in resolving such strong conflicts about authority, the clinic utilized the therapy group increasingly as an aid in placement procedures.[5]

Treating Individuals with Psychopathic Traits

In group therapy, as in individual treatment, the likelihood of effecting change appears to increase almost proportionately with the patient's closeness to classical neurotic pathology and his distance from the syndromes of extreme psychopathy. For the most part, we have not attempted at the clinic to give out-patient treatment to the true psychopath, but we have worked with a number of individuals with severe character neuroses in which there were marked psychopathic features. Agencies that do not employ the same criteria as ours for the diagnosis of a psychopathic personality might label some of these individuals as true psychopaths.

Efforts to treat these cases often are not rewarding and may even lead to dangerous acting-out episodes. We found, however, that continued contacts with some of these patients, especially those for whom there was no adequate institutional placement, sustained them through a difficult period. It also provided an opportunity to study, in a crystallized form, certain problems of pathology and treatment which are present in less severely disturbed delinquents.

Our experience with this group of patients revealed that their initial resistance is often deceptively easy to overcome. We noted in individual treatment efforts, however, that a strong resurgence of

[4] Fritz Redl, "Pre-Adolescents—What Makes Them Tick?" *Child Study,* Vol. XXI, No. 2 (1944), p. 44.

[5] See Chapter VI, p. 103.

resistance often appeared just at the point when positive feelings toward the therapist seemed to be developing and real movement appeared to be taking place. This secondary line of resistance did not seem to be designed primarily to defend the individual against the external imposition of limits, as is usually the case with the initial resistances encountered in other delinquents. Rather, this secondary resistance seemed to be a mobilization in response to the alarm about the possibility of self-deprivation or curtailment of impulse gratification. This threat, of course, became increasingly imminent as the positive feelings toward the therapist mounted. The patient, therefore, tried to find a way to escape treatment. We found that, if the indications of rising hostility are not immediately recognized and the resistance satisfactorily resolved, the individual is likely to break out into a renewed storm of delinquent behavior. These delinquencies seemed designed in part to force the imposition of severe external controls.

To prevent these adolescents from having to run into difficulty to escape the treatment relationship, the clinic has experimented with placing such young people in a therapy group just before they enter this phase of resistance. It has been found possible to discharge and resolve the hostility more constructively within the group setting than in the individual treatment situation. Following this phase, some of these adolescents were able to complete their treatment in the group setting. In other cases, it was necessary for the adolescents to return to individual treatment which then often proceeded more effectively than was possible before.

A combined individual and group approach to the treatment of a seemingly psychopathic adolescent was employed in the following case illustration.[6]

WILLIAM C

William, age 15, was brought into court by the police for stealing a small axe from a hardware store. Although the theft was a minor one, his techniques seemed to be those of an experienced burglar. He had made use of a "jimmy" and had been adept at

---

[6] In this case the boy was treated by the same therapist in individual and group therapy. This is usually desirable but not always feasible.

getting away over the rooftops and fire escapes. Previously he had been picked up on suspicion of attempting what he called a "second-story job."

William's parents were financially able to afford treatment outside the clinic but were not interested in securing it. The mother said that she felt completely unable to handle the boy and apparently hoped to use the clinic as an arm of the court to assist her in controlling him.

William's parents had been separated for about three years and divorce proceedings were pending at the time of his arrest. In their intake interviews at the clinic, both parents said that they had never really succeeded in making a satisfactory adjustment to each other despite the fact that they seemed to have entered marriage very much in love.

Sexual maladjustment had been a prominent problem. Mr. C reported that, during the early days of the marriage, his wife's sexual demands had been excessive. In recent years she had become cold and disinterested, and he felt that she responded to him only when she felt he needed an incentive to increase his earnings. Shortly before their separation, she discovered that he had been having extramarital relations. During their last year together they fought bitterly.

Both parents agreed that William's most acute difficulties—staying out late, disobedience, and stealing—seemed to date from the time of their separation (that is, about three years before, when William was just entering adolescence). There was, however, a history of early difficulties apparently related to organic disease at the time of birth. He had had post-natal jaundice for a period of two or three months, a result of a disturbance in the Rh factor which might also have caused some cerebral damage. Both parents described his first six years as characterized by marked hyperactivity and explosive aggressiveness. William's early school adjustment had been poor and he had had considerable difficulty in learning to read, in spite of his high intelligence. He had had frequent violent fights with other children.

When he was examined at the clinic he had a fine tremor of the outstretched hands, slight bilateral deafness, some minimal difficulties in hand-eye co-ordination. He scored an I.Q. of 115 with excellent verbal facility and good comprehension; his reading speed was significantly slow.

During the previous three years William had lived with his mother, visiting his father only occasionally. His actual contact with the father was slight but the mother used the father as a disciplinarian. Whenever she felt that William needed punishment, she called in the father, who administered severe beatings even though his son now almost equaled him in stature. The mother's complaints about William were that he did not obey her, was not doing his school work, and that he "snitched" small amounts of money from her to supplement his allowance. Mrs. C undoubtedly was using the boy's difficulties to demonstrate how badly William needed a father and to buttress her refusal to co-operate in divorce proceedings. She defended her frequent calls on the father with the rationalization that she was really afraid of William's mounting hostility toward her and that she had begun to fear for her own safety.

In his first interview at the clinic, William was obviously contemptuous of the entire procedure although he presented an exterior of bland affability. He had been in the office only about three minutes when the therapist lit a cigarette and offered him one. William waved it aside, looked quizzically at the therapist, and asked, "Say Doc, do you really want me to feel at ease?" The therapist looked at him inquiringly. "Well then," he said, "I wish you would stop smoking. You don't know how to do it, and you make me feel uncomfortable." William went on to talk of the attempts of some of his teachers to help him. He said he could not stand "stuffed shirts." The allusion to the therapist was unmistakable, and William needed but little encouragement to acknowledge the analogy.

Although the therapist could accept these and subsequent attacks with equanimity, the mother was becoming increasingly disturbed by William's "kidding" and in her interviews she related instances to support her contention that William's provocative behavior might lead to serious consequences. For example, she said she had been walking along the street with William when he pointed to a store and described in detail how easy it would be to break into it. Mrs. C said that when she attempted to limit his demands for money he threatened to find other, less legitimate sources of

77

income, or when she tried to discuss his school difficulties he would point out that if things became too troublesome he had a fully worked out plan for leaving home.

Despite these ominous threats and expressions of hostility toward both his mother and the therapist, William exerted sufficient control to keep out of the hands of the law while he was being seen at the clinic. These controls were not generated solely out of anxiety, fear of consequences, or desire to remain at home, but were also based on substantial ego strengths which became evident as treatment progressed.

In an interview during the second month of treatment William was talking about all the things he liked to do which were interfered with by the necessity of going to school. He talked of his interest in listening to swing records, going to the movies, and going out with girls. He complained that his mother's restrictions about hours and the school's requirements regarding attendance interfered with his enjoyment of more attractive activities. "However," he added, "even if a subject in school is dry I will work and put myself out to do things if I really like the teacher." William went on to say that he had only once failed a subject in which he had really liked the teacher and this had been because of his poor spelling, a matter that he felt powerless to improve. At the end of this session, as William turned to leave the room, he stretched and yawned and reminded the therapist that because it was a holiday he had had to get up early just to come down to the clinic. He added jokingly that it might well have been "just because I like the teacher."

As increasing manifestations of William's positive feelings toward the therapist began to appear, William began to discuss material that gave us further entree into his inner fantasy life. He had a fund of "stories" which he said that he used to dream about, particularly in the hour or so after awakening in the morning and before he got out of bed. He said these fantasies, which sometimes were accompanied by masturbation, were elaborations of stories derived from his voracious reading. One of his favorites concerned a poor boy who was mistreated by his parents and who, though he was literally starving to death, had secretly built a beautiful model of a church. No one discovered how bad the

78

parents had been or how noble the boy, until his death revealed his great works of art. There were also several other fantasies embroidered around the theme of the "bad parents" and the good but misunderstood and mistreated child.

A related theme was embodied in William's intense interest in the character of the "Saint," a figure in current detective fiction. The Saint was described by William in these terms, "He is tall, dark, and handsome, just like me. Of course I am just fooling but he's supposed to have a lot of sex appeal. He breaks up rings of criminals. He debunks the big criminals that the law can't touch but he works just as cleverly as a master criminal himself. He is a sort of Robin Hood of crime and he figures out ways to catch the big crooks. There is always a pretty girl in one of his stories. He has lots of close calls but always comes through. . . . He is a master locksmith and on locks he has *the tender touch of a loving father.* . . . Whatever he does is for the betterment of mankind. He is a crook who goes after crooks. He is a criminal who is within the law."

Consciously, William's hostility seemed to be directed entirely toward his mother; although his father gave him beatings he thought these were usually justified. Once he had even helped his father make a paddle that was to be used on his own posterior. His chief complaint against the father was that he simply was not around enough and, in this sense, he seemed to hold the father responsible for the hostility he felt toward the mother, seemingly without directing any negative feeling toward the father himself.

He often expressed resentment at the way his mother handled him. "What gets me," he said, "is that my mother expects me to act grown up and yet keeps treating me like a kid. She never lets me alone. She keeps raising all this fuss about me coming home at certain times and the crazy part of it all is that she doesn't really expect me to do it." In one session he reported that the previous evening his mother had told him to be home at six and when he got home at that time he found three places had been set at the table, one for his mother, one for his sister, and one for his mother's boy friend. He then said that his mother kept telling him how thoughtful and considerate her boy friend was and how bad William was by comparison. He said that although he was supposed

79

to have a regular allowance, his mother seemed to enjoy doling out small amounts to him so that he would have to come and ask her for each thing as he wanted it. As William enumerated instances of his mother's provocative behavior, he seemed to sense some awareness that his threats to steal or run away were actually an attempt to resolve the conflict with his mother. "I guess," he said, "I'm trying to get under her skin and I know darn well I'm doing it."

Although, as we have indicated, William referred only infrequently to his father (except in the fantasy elaborations), it was apparent, in his relationship to the therapist, that he was beginning to work out hostile feelings that were directed toward his father. On one occasion he talked about his wrestling prowess—how he was not afraid to take on two medium-sized fellows and how he had once taken on four at a time. However, he added, "No matter what kind of a fight I get into, I never let myself get angry." He then demonstrated, on the person of the therapist, how it is possible to break an arm or a back, adding with a smile, "Not that I want to sound bloodthirsty."

William's anxiety about his hostile impulses was doubtless allied to his own fear of being attacked. One may speculate about the possible origins of these fears. They may be related to his early period of development, when severe restrictions were placed by his parents upon his hyperactive motor activities. Tremendous frustrations must have been involved for this boy, whose physiological and developmental needs had been far in excess of what his parents could meet. He himself referred to his struggle to become what he called a "civilized being." His "playful" wrestling with the therapist and his jibing hostile comments directed toward him were, in a sense, the equivalent of aggressive motor play, the need for which had never been entirely fulfilled. As William's positive relationship to the therapist deepened, however, an intensification of hostile impulses toward the therapist was manifest. This secondary phase of hostility seemed to represent a struggle similar to the primitive one related to infantile frustration. This struggle, however, was enacted on a more advanced and complex psychological level. It seemed to embody some of the unresolved early problems of identification with the father and illuminated the difficulties this boy had had in making normal adolescent group identifications.

The use of the transference in the manner indicated in the therapy with William contains many dangerous elements. His hostility and explosive behavior, which were directed toward the therapist, appears to be a reaction to the imminent loss of gratification which would follow if he permitted himself to identify too closely with the therapist. It contained the risk that he would use the very elements of the therapeutic relationship to generate new hostility and ultimately to act it out in new delinquencies. This process, which has been described by Eissler, explains why delinquents become such excellent manipulators of people. Because of their strong need for pleasure and gratification, they utilize their identification with the therapist to achieve their own asocial goals.[7]

In this phase of the treatment of William—at about the third and fourth months—he seemed to be manipulating the transference situation to meet his asocial goals. He became more overtly hostile toward the therapist than he had been during his initial interviews. He criticized the therapist's taste in clothes, sketched mocking caricatures of his features, was alternately restless and apathetic during the interviews, and began to engage in symbolic but unmistakable displays of his rising hostility. During these sessions, which he attended without breaking appointments, he would shape airplanes out of sheets of paper and throw them around the room in a vengeful fashion. When one landed on the therapist's head, he was profuse in his apologies and immediately discontinued the procedure. He skilfully turned aside any attempt to interpret or point

---

[7] This is "the outcome of necessity partly in order to escape punishment which was his greatest danger and the focus of his greatest fears, and partly to achieve his aggressive goals. Therefore, a person [the therapist] who reveals himself as being superior in all these areas will become an object of admiration and interest. He [the delinquent] will know that he can obtain valuable knowledge from him and there is no limit to the knowledge the delinquent needs in order to carry out his sinister plans and nevertheless escape punishment. If the analyst can convince the delinquent of the shortcomings of the technique he had applied and impress on him that he, the analyst, knows more efficient and less dangerous techniques, the delinquent is bound to look up to him and to establish a relationship of benevolent interest as all of us do when meeting persons who represent one of our ideals. 'But,' one may object, 'admitting that this will lead to an attachment of the delinquent to his therapist, will this not merely make him a more proficient delinquent without improving his capacity for socialization?' " K. R. Eissler, M.D., in "Some Problems of Delinquency," *Searchlights on Delinquency* (K. R. Eissler, M.D., ed.), International Universities Press, New York, 1949, pp. 18–19.

up the meaning of his behavior. The therapist, naturally, feared that the acting-out behavior was not confined to the doctor's office.

These fears were borne out when the boy, who had previously been entirely regular in his attendance, began to miss appointments. The mother reported that his school difficulties, truancy, lateness, and hostility toward teachers seemed to be on the increase. She also reported that it was becoming unbearable to continue to live with him, and raised questions about the possibility of placement. William had previously made some tentative arrangements with his father about attending a boarding school in another community. The father's prospective remarriage, however, made it impossible for him to finance the plan. It also seemed unlikely that he would make a place for the boy, even as an occasional visitor, in his new home. William apparently showed no overt reaction to these stinging rejections by the father, which in itself seemed to be a serious symptom.

In this atmosphere of gathering storm and impending explosion, further treatment effort seemed almost hopeless. We then decided to try to engage him in a therapy group. Although this plan had been under consideration previously, our purpose then had been to help him work through his expressed difficulty in establishing his social relationships with his contemporaries. He had told the therapist that he was unable to think clearly in a group, was able only to listen and make an occasional comment. He had also reported that when he did talk, he would tell tall stories about imaginary travels or fancied sexual exploits. He had mentioned that he was able to maintain a relationship with the one girl he knew only with the aid of a cloak of lies about his age, school, grade, and so on. He had added that, by appearing older and more mature than he actually was, he felt more acceptable to his contemporaries. It was hoped that group therapy would assist him to make more realistic relationships.

The impasse we had reached in individual treatment led us to consider using the group for therapeutic handling of his hostility. It seemed likely that the support and the provocation of the other boys, whose aggression was less inhibited, would permit William to discharge some of his mounting and potentially explosive hostility within a relatively controlled therapeutic situation. We hoped that the group experience might avert the venting of his hostility, with possibly disastrous consequences, in the home, the school, or the community.

Therapy Group Experience

In the very first session that William attended the boys were talking about their relationships with their workers in individual treatment.

> Norman: It would be better if we did what talking we had to do just with other guys.
> Milton: Oh, sometimes it helps to talk with someone else.
> WILLIAM: Yes, sometimes it's O. K. but sometimes you get a little uneasy.
> Therapist: You mean when there's just you and someone else?
> Milton: Oh, there's nothing to it. The counselor just played cards with me all the time—pinochle. *(All the boys laugh.)*
> Robert: My guy doesn't play cards, he talks with me; sometimes it helps. It helps to know the other person's viewpoint.
> *(There is a long silence.)*
> Therapist: What do the rest of you think?
> *(William mutters something to Robert with his hand held over his mouth so the therapist cannot hear him.)*
> Robert *(somewhat angrily)*: Well, you never know if you're right until you hear the other person's view.
> WILLIAM: Well, maybe, but sometimes I just feel like saying, "Aw, the hell with it." *(The other boys grin at this defiance.)*

Later in this session the group discussed why it was they sometimes did not want to say anything in response to questions asked them in the clinic and elsewhere.

> Milton: Sometimes it's just none of their business.
> WILLIAM: Sometimes you might be afraid or you feel you can look after yourself.
> Therapist: How do you mean, afraid?
> WILLIAM: Well, you might say something that would put you in a bad light.
> Therapist: Like what sort of thing?
> WILLIAM *(after hesitating)*: Well, you know what you're gonna say, but sometimes you just don't say it.
> Robert *(belligerently)*: If I have something to say I say it.
> Therapist: Well, sometimes a guy doesn't feel like talking. . . .
> Milton: Especially if it's none of their business.
> WILLIAM: Sure, let the other fellow start the ball rolling.

In the first sessions this is what William seemed content to do. When the other boys discussed their feelings about being shoved around, William said very little. Some sessions later, however, he talked briefly about some of his experiences when he was first arrested. He told of having been hit by the policeman who discovered him in the act of stealing. He said he did not mind this, because he could understand the cop's feeling. But then, another time, a policeman came along and hit him when he was doing nothing at all, even before he questioned him. It was apparent that William felt that the officer was striking him with calculated hostility and he had great difficulty in keeping from striking back at the officer.

Meanwhile, Mrs. C reported that William was becoming more hostile toward her and that he had begun to call her obscene names. She had found a new 22-calibre rifle that William had just purchased with money he had obtained by cashing in some bonds that had been given to him. It is of interest that the first mention William made of this gun was following a group session in which he, the therapist, and several of the other boys were standing around just preparatory to leaving the clinic. Some of the other boys, particularly Robert, who had had some experience in the use of guns, became alarmed and told William that he had better watch his step and that he could really get "sent up" if he was caught using the gun without a permit. William asked the therapist to find out how to obtain a permit and where he could shoot the gun without getting into trouble. (Arrangements were subsequently made for William to join a rifle club.) Although William had refused to discuss the matter with his mother, aside from throwing out threats about what he might do with the gun, and did not approach the therapist directly, he was able to handle the question in the therapist's presence with the support of the group. In a later group session William himself helped us to understand why he was able to handle this dangerous subject in the therapy group.

> WILLIAM: When a fellow doesn't have the right understanding [at home], he just has to take all kinds of comments and everybody is always asking him why he does this or that.
> Robert: It's not the comments, it's the criticisms.
> WILLIAM: Yeah, that's it. Nobody understands.

Therapist: About what sort of thing does a person want understanding?

WILLIAM: One thing is school. A fellow doesn't want to always be harped on about homework and poor marks.

Therapist: How do the rest of you feel?

(Donald mumbles his agreement.)

WILLIAM: You wouldn't mind the comments if they'd help you figure the things out. You expect some criticisms.

Joseph: You'd want understanding if you got into trouble.

Robert: Like fighting in the street.

Therapist: You mean even if you feel you are wrong and at fault, you have a right to expect that someone gives a damn.

Robert: Sure, you expect it. After all, they went through the same thing.

WILLIAM: Sure, you expect them to realize and you want them to ask what to do, you know, so you could be sure of sympathy and understanding. Next time if you got caught you'd want somebody to confide in, but instead of that they say, "Why in hell didn't you tell us?" But you can't tell them because you were never able to confide in them.

Therapist: What gets in the way of their understanding?

WILLIAM: Worries of their own.

Robert: They don't realize how important it is. . . .

WILLIAM: My Pop was always O. K., but then I got into a serious jam.

Therapist: Would you mind being more specific?

WILLIAM *(explaining how he got caught for stealing)*: Yes, that's how I got started coming to the doctor. It was a damn serious thing. I would have expected punishment but it hurt even more when they took it calmly.

Therapist: Your mother didn't take it so calmly.

WILLIAM: I'm talking about Pop. I wouldn't have minded a beating, but it hurt more the way he took it. *(William explains that his parents are separated.)* I admit I felt a grudge when my father left. Of course I love Mom, but I couldn't discuss everything with her.

Therapist: You seem to be saying that your father may be sympathetic, but that he wasn't there very much.

From this point on William, time and again, brought into the group sessions his feelings about adults who could not be trusted, not only his own father but police, therapists, and teachers at school.

WILLIAM: Five years ago I had a swell cap pistol and I gave it to a teacher to hold for me. No, I think it was cigarettes. I didn't smoke but I got these at home for a friend. He was of age and all that *(he hestitates)* but for numerous reasons he couldn't get them. I brought them from home and not wanting to get caught with them on me I gave them to a teacher I liked in confidence. She told another teacher in confidence and then the second teacher went to the principal. I felt plenty bad about that. It's the same thing as with parents.

Therapist: Have any of the rest of you had experiences like that?

Robert: I did. I had a shotgun and when I got into trouble over it, the judge was going to let me off but my sister thought it would be nice if I were locked up for a few days. Another thing—I had a kitten for seven years that I was very attached to but when I got in trouble and was put in the detention home, the cat mysteriously died. What kind of understanding is that?

Therapist: What kind of an effect does that have on a person?

Robert: A bad effect, damn bad.

WILLIAM (chiming in): Damn bad. . . . When I used to come in late I got paddled, once for every minute late.

Donald: It isn't so terrible up to a limit.

Robert: You should ask permission to be out late for a party or something. Being punished for an extra few minutes is something else.

WILLIAM: That's right.

Donald: Yeah!

WILLIAM: Of course, now I come and go about when I want to.

Therapist: What about other things?

WILLIAM: Personally I am one of the worst shoplifters around but I wouldn't steal anything except books. Except, of course, money. (The group laughs.) I still do steal books.

For the first time William admitted that he had continued to steal. He looked around him apprehensively and then, almost as if to reassure himself, went on:

WILLIAM: I've been talking to the doctor for some time and I think what I say doesn't get beyond him. . . . Anyway I don't think my stealing of books is bad. In fact, I have no conscience about it just as long as they don't see me. I read sixteen books a week on everything from atomic research to Wild West stories, and I take the books I need. (Goes on here to discuss his techniques of stealing books.)

Robert (interrupting William and speaking in an evangelistic manner): The way I figure it there are penal sins and moral sins. (This is an interesting slip since what he obviously is referring to are venial and mortal sins.) Once in church it was explained that it was a penal (sic!) sin if you did something like taking money from a store or someone who could afford it and a moral sin when you stole from the poor. Still'n'all, a sin is a sin. Of course it isn't what you consider it. There is a commandment that says, "Thou shalt not steal." I'm not trying to be a preacher, but if you believe in religion it's a sin and if it's a sin it's bad. I still say if you stole a book, that's wrong, and if it's wrong, it's bad.

WILLIAM: Well, where do we go from here?

Joseph: If you start with books you might go on to other things.

WILLIAM: I don't think so.

Joseph: I started swiping candy from five-and-ten-cent stores. My mother used to hit me, but I didn't think it was bad. The store could afford it, I thought. Then I worked my way up to taking money from a cash register and then to burglary and then I got caught.

WILLIAM: I consider a guy a criminal who is never satisfied and takes more and more until he is caught.

Therapist: You seem to be saying it's a question of how much you get away with.

WILLIAM: I know of a counterfeiter who has been operating successfully for twenty years.

Therapist: And if he's not caught, you think it's not bad?

WILLIAM: Oh, it definitely is bad and he is at fault.

Therapist: He is?

WILLIAM: Sure, a person is responsible for what he does.

In the foregoing scene the therapy group served an interesting and unexpected function. William brought into the group precisely the kind of material that he had been using to provoke his mother. He practically bragged about his stealing and indicated that he recognized no limitations upon his impulses or desires. In so doing he seemed to be asking that limits be set for him so that he would not be able to act out the fantasy wishes that were so intimately linked to his delinquent behavior.

Traditionally the therapy group atmosphere is thought of as being permissive and encouraging the uncovering of hostile and guilt-tinged material which may sometimes not appear in the more threatening individual sessions. In this session, because the group was permissive, William was encouraged to discuss his delinquent exploits. However, in the person of Robert, the group also provided William with exactly the kind of limiting response which he appeared to be asking for and which he seemed to be trying to provoke but could not accept from either his parents or the therapist. When he finally received the response that he seemed to be demanding, it was more acceptable to him because it came from the group. This may well have been because the group had identified itself with him and he with it, in a way not easily possible in the relationship between an adult and a delinquent adolescent.

When the group discontinued its regular session for the summer, William resumed individual treatment. It soon became evident that the character of his relationship to the therapist had changed markedly. His ambivalence had almost completely disappeared and he seemed to have very little need for many of the defenses that were evident in the pre-group phase of individual treatment. He was increasingly able to express his long-repressed negative feelings toward his father and it was possible for him to drop his mask of indifference toward him. He began to make a number of realistic demands upon his father and at the same time was less disturbed by his mother's nagging and provocations. For example, he handled her habit of doling out money to him by deciding to get a part-time job. Facing up to his real feelings toward his father seemed to lessen his need to displace certain negative feelings onto his mother; it also increased his readiness to attempt to resolve fantasy wishes that had been directed both toward her and toward the therapist.

William became outspoken in his demands that his father spend more time with him. The father responded with some warmth and promised that when he remarried, William would be welcome in his home. All this seemed to contribute markedly to diminishing William's tension and hostility. Also, he made some improvement in his school work and, with the promise of help from his father, he again began to plan for further education at a school away from the city.

The group experience can be viewed as an intrinsic part of the total treatment. It provided a means to sustain contact when his mobilized hostility was motivating him to flight and possibly serious acting-out behavior. It also assisted him to become more independent while, at the same time, it provided gratification for certain of his dependency needs. His capacity to relate to his peers in a meaningful and realistic way was significantly improved. The group experience thus was an aid in developing his potential for both independence and interdependence, which is the goal of all psychotherapeutic efforts.

VI. Group Therapy with Parents

In both theory and practice it is difficult to separate the parental relationship from the total life experience of the two parents. Especially is this true when they have suffered the kinds of severe deprivation that critically interfere with being the type of "good parent" that society demands. Even the most "rejecting" parent who comes to an agency insisting that his child be put away, may be expressing many needs and feelings not directly related to the child. The discerning worker detects in the parent elements of deep positive involvement with his child, even though he may be literally casting him out of the house.

When a child has engaged in delinquent acts, the feelings of the parents are likely to be highly ambivalent, with the negative feelings in the ascendancy. Regardless of the setting in which they are seen, the parents usually have considerable resistance to looking at their feelings or involvements with the child or at other family difficulties. The resistance tends to become intensified when any attempt is made to focus the discussion on their own personal problems. They often seem almost entirely unable to acknowledge that any problems exist and they frequently have deferred seeking help until they were literally forced to do so by the child's difficulties with the community. Thus, the same forces that led to the child's difficulty also give rise to a type of resistance to treatment which is almost insurmountable.

The clinic's program of group therapy for parents was initiated in the hope that a therapy group might provide a means of overcoming the obstacle of resistance.[1] As with the children's groups, the first therapy groups for parents were designed to reach persons who were failing to derive benefit from individual treatment, or who seemed incapable of being drawn into treatment. In a number of cases, the parents selected were sabotaging the treatment of the child to such an extent that progress was impossible.

Testing the Value of Therapy Groups

Sometimes we used the sort of impasse that we had encountered in individual treatment not only as the criterion for selection but also as a rather unusual device for referring the parents to the group. Since they had not only failed to obtain help in treatment but were often actively hostile to the court, the clinic, and the worker, we utilized their dissatisfaction as the point of departure for discussing the group sessions. We told these parents that others had similar complaints and that we thought it might be helpful for a number of them to meet with a staff member for an exchange of views. Subsequently, they were formally invited to attend such a session.

At the early sessions, the therapist, when he was angrily pressed for "answers" to questions, would readily concede that the clinic did not know how to solve all problems but that both he and the staff were interested in the parents' opinions; perhaps solutions could be found if they worked together.

From the clinic's standpoint, these group sessions drew attention to many difficulties that the staff had previously neglected. Other problems were seen in startlingly new perspective when presented from the vantage point of the parents. The fact that the therapist was outnumbered by individuals who had certain common experiences placed him in the position of listener and observer, which literally forced him to re-examine his preconceptions. The disparity between his own concepts of reality and reality as presented by the

[1] All the parents' groups discussed in this section were composed exclusively of mothers. A few fathers were included in some of the therapy groups at the clinic. The difficulty of arranging evening hours in the court building precluded greater participation by fathers in the group therapy program.

group was often great, and served as a corrective to his thinking of certain experiences of the patient as distortions. The opportunity for the therapist to engage in this kind of critical scrutiny of the client's life experiences gave direction to the subsequent work in the therapy groups, and also led to modifications of procedures in individual treatment.[2]

The case of Mrs. Phillips was selected for presentation to illustrate some of the potentials of group therapy with certain parents of delinquent youngsters. It also illustrates some problems of method which we encountered in the first project. Subsequently, as the program developed, various changes in approach were made. (See the case of Mrs. Foster, p. 132.)

MRS. PHILLIPS

Mrs. Phillips, the mother of Richard who was brought to court at the age of 15, might be characterized as a "good" woman. She had shown great strength in the face of almost overwhelming hardships. When Richard was only 3, Mr. P left home to join a cult, taking Richard with him. Mrs. P seemed to share the belief of the cult and for several years prior to the separation she and her husband had lived as "sister and brother." She said that she missed her son, as well as her husband, after the father took him away. Two years after Richard's departure, she made a trip to a distant city and daringly kidnapped the boy from the nursery where Mr. P had placed him. It might be noted that Mrs. P stated that when the boy returned home he seemed dull and apathetic. During two years of early childhood, a critical period in development, Richard

2 At this writing it appears that, of all the parents who had failed in individual treatment and were subsequently referred for group therapy, a little over 50 per cent showed some significant degree of improvement three years after the beginning of the project. Observable progress appeared to vary anywhere from marked changes in basic personality structure, with corresponding alteration in the entire family constellation, to transitory movement within circumscribed areas and limited carryover into the parent-child relationship. As indicated previously (footnote, p. 68), about 60 per cent of the adolescents who were placed in therapy groups after failing in individual treatment also achieved varying degrees of improvement. Although these were not carefully controlled studies, the results seemed sufficiently rewarding so that we were encouraged to expand greatly the use of group therapy in the clinic.

91

was probably without adequate maternal care, which may have been a determinant in the development of the picture of extreme psychopathy which he presented.

Mrs. P felt that she would have to be both mother and father to the child. Her income, derived from domestic labor, was supplemented by a public welfare allowance. When she was away at work, her son was under the supervision of a neighbor or a feeble-minded aunt. Despite these strains, Mrs. P participated in the work of her church and talked constantly of her high moral standards. She had occasional extra-marital relationships about which she was extremely guilty, and did not like to acknowledge, even to herself, that her daughter, who was conceived several years after Mrs. P's separation from her husband, had really been born out of wedlock. At times she engaged in small deceptions to maintain her income at a higher level than the welfare department allowed. Because of her strict upbringing these deceptions created considerable guilt and intensified her determination that her children should be models of filial obedience and spiritual purity. She found herself becoming increasingly strict, irritable, and even mean in her handling of Richard. She could not tolerate his childish "wildness." She joked about her son's possessive attitude toward her but actually was very much disturbed by it. She said that she probably would never be able to get married until Richard gave his "permission." As she grew older, it became increasingly difficult for her to assume her own household duties at the end of a long day's work. She began to insist that the children, and Richard particularly, take some responsibility for the housework. As she said in a therapy group session, "I never had the privilege of sitting around my house all day long or just staying home to make dinner ready for my kids, so I had to be strict with them. Now maybe I never will have any satisfactions from them because I was so strict, but I hope I will be forgiven for it."

Mrs. P was stunned one day when she asked Richard to mop the kitchen floor and he rebelled. He did not talk back, for (as Mrs. P said in court) he was a boy who "never in his whole life gave a fresh answer to his mother." He had accepted punishment and beatings silently and with apparent meekness. This time, however, he ran away and remained away from the home for four months. She

92

knew he was in the neighborhood but was too proud, hurt, and angry to ask him to come back. She was apprehensive about him but did not admit, even to herself, that he might be doing something illegal to support himself. Four months after he had left home he was arrested for attempted rape, assault, and robbery. He had followed a middle-aged woman along a deserted street, jumped on her from behind, dragged her to the ground, and begun to tear the clothes from her. Richard told the police that he had hoped to frighten the woman into giving him money but that he probably would have raped her, had he not been detected by a policeman and arrested.

The psychiatrist at the detention home noted Richard's marked impulsiveness and his tendency to live for the moment. He seemed to require instant gratification of all his desires and was unable to tolerate any tension. He did not appear to learn from experience and tended to repeat his impulsive behavior again and again. The examination at the clinic confirmed these impressions. The boy was a severe psychopath and the pathology appeared to be well fixed. Prognosis was poor and he seemed unsuited either for probation or for out-patient treatment at the clinic. There appeared to be no alternative but commitment to the state training school, although it was recognized that the defects in Richard's personality would probably not be mended by the arbitrarily imposed authority of a training school experience.

At this point Mrs. P intervened strenuously. She pleaded valiantly with everyone for her son to be given "another chance." The case was re-evaluated at the insistence of the probation officer in response to the mother's pleas. She insisted that Richard was really a good boy at heart and that she would beat him within an inch of his life if he ever again dared stray from the straight and narrow path.

In the light of the prognosis, it would be difficult to justify the use of clinic time for treatment of this boy. The case was accepted, however, largely because of research interest in exploring further whether there were any possible modifications in treatment approach which might offer a better alternative to the "blind alley" inherent in the institutional placements available. We also wanted to know whether group therapy with the parents of such children would yield results that would suggest that we alter our practice of not allotting clinic time for the treatment of such cases.

A plan was devised in which both mother and son were to be seen no less than once, and the boy up to three times, each week at the clinic. On days when he was not seen at the clinic he was to be seen by the probation officer who would check carefully on his activities. Conferences to integrate these activities at first were held every week and later every month. They were attended by the psychiatrist who saw the boy in individual treatment, the caseworker assigned to the mother, the probation officer, the chief psychiatric social worker at the clinic, and the probation officer's supervisor.

At no time during the contact with this case was there much optimism about its progress. From the outset the workers were continuously impressed by the vast amount of resistance precipitated even in the initial contacts with this family. It may be of interest to categorize this resistance in some detail.[3]

1. *Denying or minimizing the problem:* In her first interview Mrs. P began to paint Richard as a reformed character. She said that since he had returned from the detention home he had been very good. She feared he might have changed while he was away and become "fresh" but she was relieved to find that he was just as he had been. When she was able to concede there was any difficulty at all, she tended to ascribe Richard's difficulty to "boyhood pranks." By a remarkable sleight-of-hand she succeeded at one and the same time in denying that Richard had had any failings and in insisting that he had completely recovered from them.

2. *Criticism of the clinic and its methods:* Hardly had Mrs. P's pleas that Richard be seen at the clinic been granted than she was protesting angrily against the necessity for his attendance. She was sure he felt "hemmed in and watched." She began to offer explanations in advance of why Richard might be unable to keep an appointment and said with a smile she knew the clinic "would understand."

[3] The five categories of resistance outlined here are taken from "Study of Resistance in Five Mothers to the Early Phase of Treatment at the Psychiatric Treatment Clinic of Manhattan Children's Court," a Professional Project by Elizabeth Eckart, New York School of Social Work of Columbia University, New York, April, 1948.

3. *Blocking communication by breaking appointments, lateness, silence, and so on:* Both mother and son began to miss appointments with increasing frequency. The boy would say he had failed to understand the time agreed upon or that he had taken the wrong train or that they would not excuse him from school. When he ran out of excuses, the mother supplied them: The snow was too heavy or Richard did not have rubbers or she thought he might have a test in school that day.

4. *Challenging the clinic:* In her very first interview, Mrs. P made clear the role that she assigned to the clinic when she said that she, as the closest person to Richard, could tell the worker exactly what Richard needed and that she knew how to raise children since she had had two and raised them all right. She made it clear that no one could tell her or her children what to do. She said her children would do exactly what she said because she was the boss.

5. *Denying any personal involvement or responsibility in the problem—showing other persons or factors to be responsible:* Mrs. P indicated her apartness from Richard's problem during the first minutes of an early interview. When asked about her feelings toward the clinic in reference to herself, she answered with conviction, "Naturally I am O.K. mentally." She explained to the worker that this must be so since she was older and therefore her brain was more developed than that of her son. The only reason she saw for her appointments was to impart information that the clinic might require in its work with Richard. Her guarded attitude was expressed when she said, "Every day I expect the policeman to come to my door." Over approximately nine months of contact in individual treatment she never really relinquished this guard. At the end of this period Mrs. P's worker reported that she was still quite insistent that Richard was making an excellent adjustment and that she was unwilling to accept any further help from the clinic. The worker concluded, "It seems that Mrs. P has taken everything from the therapeutic relationship that her own hostility will allow."

As contact with Mrs. P proceeded, it seemed as if each step in the treatment process intensified her resistance in a number of areas. Treatment not only re-precipitated her concern over her failure as a mother and her guilt around her drives toward Richard, but it also sharpened the anxiety that seemed diffusely distributed throughout her total life situation. The inappropriate guilt could not be directly acknowledged in any way. Although awareness of the reality basis of some of her difficulties might have served to relieve some of Mrs. P's guilt and anxiety, this was difficult to achieve in the face of her need to deny the very existence of a "problem."

In deciding to place Mrs. P in a therapy group, it was felt that a group, by its very nature, might lend itself more easily to the solution of the dilemma described above. In a group, materials too dangerous to be examined directly by the patient may be introduced by others. The patient has the opportunity of examining them under the guise of impersonality. The opportunity of talking about other people's problems thus permits an approach to critical material without premature exposure of one's own concerns. The other patients take on roles in relation to the clinic and the therapist which the patient himself is apprehensive about assuming. However, the protections afforded by this kind of group process are certainly not all-encompassing and, as the material presented below demonstrates, they can be extended only to a certain degree in assisting a parent whose resistances are as well crystallized as were those of Mrs. P.

Therapy Group Experience

In the very first session that Mrs. P attended, the group was examining the general conditions that contribute to delinquency.

Mrs. A: I think the neighborhood has everything to do with it. Yes, everything. Another thing is money. The children want what other children have. For example, Kay wants a jacket like the other kids have but I can't buy it for her. She has a jacket that is two years old. I don't have money to get her anything better. . . . There are so many things for the kids to want nowadays. We didn't have moving-picture shows or so many special clothes when I was a young girl. Things are entirely different now.

Therapist: What do the rest of you think?

MRS. P (*nodding her head in confirmation*): Children have indecent company and this comes because we don't have a decent income. The relief allowance is always bad, not enough to live on in a decent neighborhood. If you want to live in a better place you have to get the extra rent money yourself and I just can't do this. The relief doesn't give you the very necessities for living, to say nothing of some of the extra things. The children ask you for money for things they really need to bring to school and I can't furnish it. This makes me feel very bad and embarrassed. When the children want and need money so bad, this drives them to get it in the wrong way.

Mrs. A: I swear to God that children are driven to do such things but, when I see it, it makes me mad and I think of what the Bible says that if you spare the rod you spoil the child, and that we should bring up the child in the way he is taught. . . .

Mrs. B: And sometimes the money makes them bad. My daughter wants things and asks me for them but I can't give them to her. This is what makes trouble.

MRS. P (breaks in): May I say something? (Turns to therapist, who nods.) I think sometimes it is the parents' fault. I feel that young girls should have young boys up to the house and then they don't have to go around outside and get into trouble. Then we can give them some of the things that you and I didn't have when we were young. (Melodramatically) I'll tell you what I do for my boy. I make sandwiches and mix up a big bowl of fruit punch. I get twenty-five cents worth of sacramental wine and mix it up with fruit juice and soda in a big punch bowl and put it in the middle of the table and let them eat and drink and play and dance just as they want to. Then I can see what they are doing and they are in their own home. If you will do that, they will bring their friends up and it will keep them in the house instead of on the street.

Up to this point Mrs. P had obviously been dealing with material with which she was comfortable. One is tempted to say that the position she initially took was a false one. Her elaborate discussion of the bad conditions within her neighborhood, her picture of herself as the thoughtful, permissive mother, seemed like downright deception. Yet, both of these things had an element of truth in them. The group at least seemed to have no question that the conditions to which Mrs. P referred did have a part in twisting their children's lives and personalities. It should be noted, however, that Mrs. P probably had seldom arranged the kind of party she spoke of for Richard. Nevertheless, it may not have been because she did not want to. The recognition that was accorded her reality difficulties by the group seemed to provide Mrs. P with strength and support. She turned to the therapist and challenged him directly.

MRS. P: Now I don't have any trouble with my boy (then nods to therapist and goes on proudly). Remember, I told you you got to give me a chance and I've had no trouble with my son since then. I know I whipped him and you don't believe in whipping, do you? But I do! I know what my father done and I stand on the Bible. I kiss the Book that says "Spare the rod and spoil the child." I do! And I don't have any trouble with him anymore. I don't know why I even have to come to the clinic. The reason I brought him here the first time wasn't serious and now I sometimes wonder why I brought him here at all. The only trouble I have with him is when I try to get him to help clean the house. That's when he ran away the first time. But that's one thing I expect him to do—to clean the house. He doesn't want to wash the dishes and clean that little hallway, but I can't kill him for that.

Mrs. A: We need clinics like this and doctors like the doctor here to help us. I know for myself, I have gotten a lot of good out of the clinic. It's a hard job to be a mother and there are things we cannot answer and figure out. So it is nice to have somebody like you, doctor, to tell us about life and nature and why our children do the things they do.

It will be noted that Mrs. P, in confronting the therapist, mustered two great authorities in her support—her strict father and the morality of the Bible. In so doing she protected herself in her first challenge to the therapist. It was not she who was defying him, but rather her gods, whom she was turning loose on him. However, even in this very first session, although the therapist did not take up her challenge, other members of the group—like Mrs. A—whose life situations more closely paralleled Mrs. P's, did begin to indicate some difference from the position that she took. Since Mrs. P partially identified with them she felt she must pay them some heed, and so she perfunctorily permitted herself to agree with Mrs. A.

As a result, Mrs. P's declaration of faith in her familiar authorities was somewhat weaker than her first statement. Even this minute movement was in itself a very threatening thing and at the next meeting Mrs. P did not arrive until the women were already leaving the building. She hurried upstairs to the clinic, sought out the therapist, and told him breathlessly that she had met the ladies downstairs and she knew that the meeting was over but that she came up to show the therapist that she had not really forgotten; it was just that she overslept. Thus she made her obeisance before the new gods. She was hoping to continue to keep herself from being destroyed just in case this new magic should really prove to be all-powerful. She felt she must contrive to appease the group without actually participating in it, which she thus far had succeeded in doing.

When she arrived (somewhat late) for the next meeting, she

98

found the group talking in approving terms of the importance of kindness, permissiveness, and understanding on the part of parents. Mrs. P seemed anxious to enter into the spirit of the meeting and immediately upon her arrival launched into descriptions of her elaborate plans for being the perfect mother. The group recognized what she was doing, however, and continued to press her for details of her relationship to her son.

To defend herself, she brought out more and more of the circumstances around the episode that finally brought Richard into court.

> MRS. P: My boy stayed away from the house for four months. He would come to the house with money for his sister but I wouldn't even go to the door. I just looked out the window but I didn't talk to him. I let him stay out there. He's got to come in from the outside and come in under my jurisdiction if he wants anything from me. He just brought shame on me when he was with me. He disgraced me when he brought me down here.

As Mrs. P related this incident she became aware that she was shocking most of the other women in the group. She suddenly recognized that she had permitted herself to move into a position that set her apart from the others. She became frightened and panicky.

> MRS. P: I think all children do things that they shouldn't do. You have to expect it. I know when I was a kid I did little things that were wrong but there was always a reason for it.

In this statement, although she began by talking about her son, she seemed to end by pleading for the group to understand that though she had done something wrong there were reasons for it. Some of these reasons she had already established in the long, preceding discussions about terrible conditions existing in her neighborhood and the difficulties of a husbandless mother in bringing up a child.

Despite the increased permissiveness of the atmosphere of the group Mrs. P's attendance continued to be irregular. However, in a meeting that she did attend several months after the session just described, she was able to proceed to a more direct examination of some very disturbing concerns which she had managed to conceal up to this time.

Mrs. C had been telling the group about how she tried to treat

99

all her children equally, when Mrs. P broke in to claim similar honors but then, surprisingly, went on to admit to a very painful mistake.

> MRS. P: I never gave one child any more attention than I gave the other; I don't think so.
>
> Mrs. C: Well, I didn't think that I had either but I know that I must have missed up somewhere along the line.
>
> MRS. P: No, I was more careful than you were, but remember that in your case both of them are your husband's children. Maybe you have the father of both of the children. My children are half sister and half brother and I know the slightest bit of attention that I pay to one more than I pay to the other they catch me, so I'd always be careful.

Here Mrs. P, for the first time in our contact with her, acknowledged that her two children did not have the same father. Since she had had only one husband, this admission was an exceedingly painful one. Furthermore, she went on to make clear why it was that she had to "lean over backward" so hard in her treatment of Richard that she ended by breaking broomsticks over his back in her efforts to suppress, and even beat out of existence, certain words, feelings, and thoughts.

> MRS. P: Yes, but one other thing, he didn't want me to get married. He always differed on that. He would come up to me and speak about that. Even when he was 5 years old. I remember I told him I was going to get married and he cried like everything then. About last May I think it was, he came around the house and asked me "Are you going to get married?" and I explained to him that I might. He said, "Well, he seems to be a nice man but I don't know whether you should get married or not." He never gave me a complete "go ahead" to get married. He never has, even right up to today, and he is almost 17 years old.
>
> Mrs. C: Well, maybe he's jealous. That's nature and that started a long time ago.
>
> MRS. P: Since he was 5 years old, he has resented adults. I don't care how nice a person would be to him—a mailman, he treated him ever so nice—it didn't make any difference. He'll be nice to a man as long as I don't mention that I am going to get married. If I do that, that's all. He'll never like them again. He don't care how nice they've been.

Richard thus became the scapegoat for the working out of his mother's own conflicts, in the course of which she was almost compelled to force him into the mold of the outwardly complacent boy, superficially submissive to her uncompromising authority. When the pressures within Richard grew sufficiently great, they

100

exploded in a way that understandably surprised this mother who was so proud of her son who "never had spoken a fresh word." That she was so shocked by this development was an indication of the strength of the repressive forces that began to diminish somewhat as she progressed in the therapy group. This movement was evidenced in the session in which Mrs. P gave her version of the act that finally brought Richard into court.

MRS. P: Well, that was the whole thing; he explained it to me. He said he wasn't after the money so much. He didn't know what happened. This woman was going into her apartment and he started to rape her. *And she is a woman my age, maybe a little older.* That's the part I can't see why. I could see him trying to break into a place to try to get something to eat, but for a boy 15 years old—why would his passion get so high that he'd grab a woman of that age? I don't know whether—I feel that he must have been after the pocketbook. And he let the woman talk because he won't deny anything, you know. Everything that that detective says to him he says "Yes!" I'm the mother—but a 15-year-old boy—I think it must have been for her money. After all he didn't have anything. When he was away from the home he never came back to the house to get any clothes or anything. People always used to tell me, "Oh, he looked so fine, it's a wonder you don't go out and find out for yourself how nice he looks." When he came back he had some pants, a sweater, everything. He was out stealing. When he was home he didn't have to steal. But when he went out in the world and he was all alone he had to do something.

Mrs. P had for the present explained, as well as she could, the complex welter of feelings that had been boiling inside her all these years. Certainly, she had exposed a great deal more of herself than it seemed possible for her to do in the individual treatment situation. In spite of this, she seemed unable to go beyond this point. In some of the following sessions she seemed to be trying to explain the nature of her impasse. She re-emphasized and stressed the barrenness of her life, the need for seemingly endless work, the lack of opportunity for satisfaction in the community or in her home and her children. She spoke again and again of bad conditions in her neighborhood, the inadequate relief allowance, the struggle to meet her children's requirements in the midst of poverty. This material cannot be dismissed solely as resistance, for it reflects those aspects of reality which limited Mrs. P's movement both within her own world and within the treatment situation.

In trying to explain her role in relation to the children she said:

MRS. P: I really feel myself that the children think I'm mean, though I said to them only last night, "You treat me like I'm treating you. You treat me like a stepmother and I treat you like stepchildren." I'm tired of hearing my own voice yelling in the house. I can't get those children to do anything, they just sit there and read.

Mrs. D: There shouldn't be so much work or trouble just for three people.

MRS. P: My son won't do anything any more, he just laughs, and I have no husband to tell him what to do.

Mrs. C: I didn't always have a husband either, he was always running around.

MRS. P: At least you had a piece of a husband and that's better than none at all. . . . It's just important to let them know they have a father, even if he walked in and walked out again.

Mrs. C: A man can do wrong and then pick himself up and be all right, but it's not easy for a woman to do that . . . but I agree if there are two or three children, then it's good to have your husband. I mean you want a man in the house. . . . Maybe it's because of the money or something.

In a later session the group talked about their various neighborhoods and their effect on the behavior of their children.

Mrs. D: In my neighborhood all you can see today are the Italians and the Irish.

Mrs. C: That's what I'm trying to tell you, it's a mixed neighborhood.

Therapist: Are you saying then that it's not the nationality of the people that is the cause?

Mrs. D: That's right, it happens just the same.

MRS. P (strongly): The majority of the people in the neighborhood where children get into trouble are poor people. . . . Maybe, like me, they do everything trying to make the children happy and when it doesn't seem to be any use at all I just go out and work, work, work, and when the children are bad I whip them even though I know it doesn't do any good. I have nobody to advise me, and I would like to know more ideas about all this. I would really like to know.

In the therapy group experience the clinic may have succeeded in relieving Mrs. P of some of the more inappropriate guilt and anxiety, and thus enabled her to relax for a time her rigid defenses and impossible demands upon her children. In addition, the treatment plan for the boy surrounded him with institution-like safeguards; the frequent visits to and from the probation officer, together with the aid of the therapist, ultimately helped Richard to work through some of his more superficial problems of adjustment. Richard kept out of difficulty for several years, but then he was picked up on a charge of breaking and entering. It is difficult to assess whether treatment made any real contribution to this family, although it is hoped that as a result of Mrs. P's treatment the younger child may have a somewhat better chance of survival than her brother.

Mrs. P herself made it clear that she needed much more than insight or freedom from guilt since so many of the forces that thrust her into pathology continued to operate against her. She still had to function as a woman in a man's world, as a Negro in a white world. She still had to compete in the labor market while she was trying to be a homemaker for her family. She had to search desperately for even meager gratifications on any level of life. Apparently, the therapy group was either too threatening, or not meaningful enough, to permit her to attend with sufficient regularity, duration, or participation to achieve any really strong group identifications. However, if Mrs. P is ever to extract more satisfactions from life for herself or for her children than she has hitherto been able to attain, she desperately needs the help of other people. As she herself has said, "Alone, the struggle is a lonely and hopeless one."

Preparation of Parent for Child's Placement

The disturbances that occur during the placement of an adolescent are often a dramatic condensation of the more prolonged struggles that have taken place in the family over a period of years. The period during which placement is being planned and carried out, therefore, is usually one of fiercely intensified conflicts. If these are not adequately resolved, placement may be doomed to failure even before the adolescent leaves his home. Group therapy with the parents is often of considerable help in dealing productively with the intensified guilt and other conflicts precipitated by the consideration of placement. Although the resolution of such feelings is, of course, important to the participation of the parents in a constructive placement experience, it becomes even more essential when there is some expectation that the child may ultimately be able to return to the home.

103

The task of the worker in such cases is a difficult one. The parent is frequently so ashamed and guilty over the placement that he is unable even to talk about it to friends and relatives. Or, if he does so, he must conceal precisely those feelings over which he is most conflicted. In other words, he must hide, not only from others but also from himself, his actual role in the placement process. Such denial and distortion will inevitably be reflected in the child's own feelings about leaving the home and, hence, increase his disturbance. The difficulties encountered by the worker in attempting to gain access to the parent's real feelings are, of course, related to the fact that the worker is seen by the parent as an agent who has been instrumental in effecting the placement. Since the worker represents authority, the parent's characteristic attitudes toward authority obviously will determine the role in which they cast him. Usually the parent presents a great deal of self-justification and has a strong need to deny any rejection of the child or any deficiencies as a parent. Despite himself, the parent is frequently impelled to distort and exaggerate the child's role while at the same time he suppresses his own personal problems which may have contributed to the need for placement of the child.

Group therapy can help both the child and the parent work through these problems on a more realistic level. In the therapy group, the child is often able to abandon his insistence that "They are sending me away because I was bad." He is able to achieve some sense of his own identity as a person, as he is helped to view himself through the eyes of other members of the group. He is, thus, able to differentiate reality from the self-evaluations derived from his negative experiences within the family, which often have been reinforced by subsequent unpleasant happenings at school and in the community.

The parent, who has the opportunity to examine his own life experiences in relation to his difficulties with the child, may be freed from the need to defend himself frantically against feelings of guilt and a sense of failure as a parent. He may then have less need to project and displace the entire burden onto the child. The therapy group facilitates both these processes because its structure permits the parent to work through both peer and authority relationships simultaneously; it may therefore contribute to the solution of problems exceedingly difficult to solve in individual treatment and consequently increase the likelihood of a constructive placement experience.

The following case is presented to illustrate various aspects of the group therapeutic process with the parents of an adolescent who was being prepared for placement. The discussion of the process, however, has not been restricted solely to the problems of placement since other aspects of group treatment with parents are illustrated in this case.

MRS. MANTON

Both Mrs. Manton and her son Fred, age 13, had been receiving individual treatment for about a year when she began to examine the possibility that it might be best if he were removed from the home. Although some progress appeared to have been made in individual treatment with Mrs. M, this very progress seemed to have contributed to an intensification of the conflicts within the family in a way that seemed likely to interfere with the benefits to be anticipated from placement of the child.

Fred M was brought into court because he had broken into a house with several other boys and had stolen almost a thousand dollars worth of silverware. After he was on probation for some months, the probation officer reported that he seemed indifferent about his offense, was truanting, and was having difficulty in school, and that his family situation seemed to be very disturbed. He received frequent and severe beatings at the hands of his father, felt that he was being continuously blamed by his mother, and was extremely jealous of a younger sister whom he regarded as the favored sibling. He was a boy of dull normal intelligence and clearly the least attractive of the children. In addition, a great deal of the conflict between the parents had apparently been projected onto him.

Mrs. M had been born in a small town in the Midwest. Her mother had died when Mrs. M was quite young, and she and a sister had taken charge of the household duties for their father. She was under 16 when she became engaged to Mr. M, who shortly thereafter entered military service. During Mr. M's absence, she became

105

pregnant with Fred's older brother. Subsequently, she tried to break the engagement with Mr. M, telling him of her pregnancy, but he insisted (and she agreed) that they go through with the marriage. No sooner were they married, however, than it became evident that he had been motivated by considerations other than those of love or magnanimity. He constantly reminded her of her indiscretion and of how undeserving she was of his generosity. The demands he placed upon her, both sexually and otherwise, were harsh and inconsiderate. He began to drink heavily and would torment her with unfounded accusations of her continuing infidelity. After their second child, Fred, was born Mr. M, when intoxicated, would question Fred's paternity and shout foul epithets at his wife and newborn child.

These disturbances within the family continued throughout Fred's childhood, and Mrs. M became an increasingly anxious and insecure person. She began to lose weight, to complain of insomnia and gastrointestinal disturbances, to neglect her appearance, and to play a beaten and submissive role both in her family and in life in general. She seemed to accept her lot and her husband's abuse as a just punishment for her premarital affair, but was somewhat less resigned to her husband's vicious treatment of Fred and the other children. She seemed powerless, however, to oppose Mr. M or to offer Fred the protection or love she felt toward him She felt entirely incapable of handling the situation, and in a sort of desperation, began to join Mr. M in abusing Fred as if by so doing she could divert some of the attacks from herself.

For about a year Mrs. M and Fred were seen weekly in individual treatment at the clinic. During this period, Fred was able to set up a deepening relationship with his worker and verbalized some of his feelings about his parents. He became somewhat less anxious, and he no longer stole. His school adjustment, however, continued to be very poor. He was usually in trouble with teachers and truanted frequently, for which he received severe beatings from his father.

It proved impossible to bring Mr. M into treatment. He came to the clinic only when some critical situation concerning the boy emerged. He continued to use Fred's delinquency as a weapon in his attacks on Mrs. M and for working out his own feelings of inadequacy. Mrs. M, in the course of treatment, began to have some sense of the way that Fred was being exploited but seemed powerless to alter the pattern. She confessed that her abuse of Fred had become a device that enabled her to remain with her husband, whom she hated but whom she feared to leave. She pointed out that she had never really earned her own living and that she dreaded being left with a family of children to depend on a meager public assistance income or on a husband who would be reluctant to contribute.

Mrs. M began to feel that it might be best if Fred were removed from the home. Her inner guilt, however, which was intensified by her increased awareness of her own role in Fred's difficulties, made it exceedingly difficult for her to take this step. She felt that Fred's placement would confirm the fact that she had failed—first as a daughter, then as a wife, and now as a mother as well.

The clinic felt that placement might well be indicated for Fred but recognized that it could only be regarded by him as the final act of punishment by his father and as a further rejection by the mother who seemed neither to protect nor to love him.

In placing Mrs. M in a therapy group it was hoped that she might be helped to modify some of the patterns within the home, and to provide Fred with a more positive experience than the almost total rejection that he had thus far experienced from both parents. This change on her part, it was felt, would improve Fred's chances for a successful placement and increase the possibility that he might be able later to return to the home.

Therapy Group Experience

During Mrs. M's first group session she sat through the entire meeting without saying a word. Several other women were also attending for the first time and the discussion was a rather general one. Nevertheless, the situation must have been very threatening to Mrs. M, who sat off in a corner, her shoulders hunched in a slightly cringing posture, her eyes fixed on the floor in front of her. From time to time, she plucked imaginary lint from the sleeve of her dress.

When Mrs. M finally did talk, in the second session she attended, it was in a voice so low as to be a little above a whisper, and it

107

was necessary for the group to lean foward to catch even an occasional word.

Mrs. B had been talking of how ashamed she had been because the doctor at a hospital where her boy was receiving treatment for a medical condition had referred disparagingly to her son's court record.

> Mrs. B: My son, he thinks it's a shame to be on probation. He doesn't want anybody to know he's on probation.
> MRS. M: Yes, it makes them feel very bad. . . .
> Mrs. B: Oh, I think it's a shame. . . .
> MRS. M: Yes, it's a shame. . . . Another boy and mine got into trouble and mine got all the publicity. . . .
> Mrs. B: Sure, it's a shame.
> MRS. M: Nobody is perfect in this world; we all have to try to do our best. Regardless of what happens, I love my boy. I felt bad for the way he acted because he acted so bad, but I'm hoping he's changed. People have told him he did wrong, and he sees that it wasn't good but it's my husband that . . . . I don't know why but when his father isn't there he's so nice. Sometimes he really is better.
> Therapist: You mean when his father is away?
> MRS. M: Yes. I think that his father tried to make him too good and has been after him too much. Everything the boy did his father took out on me and he kept after me too much, too.
> Therapist: You mean every time the child did something wrong you would be blamed?
> MRS. M: Yes, I couldn't keep track of him all the time. He'd be in school part of the day. I couldn't do any more than I was doing. It was impossible. Sometimes my husband would just watch to see if he would get into trouble.

It was evident here that Mrs. M's concern and shame over Fred's difficulties were intimately related to her own guilt and her husband's continuous recriminations. She might have felt that if Fred were sent away to an institution it would have been tantamount to her confessing to the world that her husband's accusations were true and that her youthful indiscretions had made her into a person unfit to be a mother.

Some sessions later, in the course of a discussion about whether or not children had a right to talk back or express feelings of resentment to their parents, Mrs. M made it clear that this problem was of interest to her, not only as it pertained to Fred, but even more as it related to her own role in the family and in her relations to others.

108

Mrs. C: Our children are not the only ones who act up when they get angry. We parents do, too. Sometimes we might break a picture or a chair or something or throw something at the person we are angry at and often we don't think of what we do in a fit of anger. I know how it is myself, but we adults have enough control not to harm anybody, but children might not, you know. . . .

Therapist: And the rest of you?

Mrs. B: I just yell.

MRS. M: I don't eat when I get mad. I'm not the kind that shows my troubles, but sometimes I can't keep the children from seeing how I feel.

Therapist: Well, although we're not all alike and don't all have the same problems, we seem to have certain things in common. Those of us who don't eat may not be feeling too different from those who yell or throw chairs.

(Mrs. C laughs and nods.)

MRS. M: Well, I get a nervous and upset stomach when I am angry.

Mrs. C: My children do that, too.

MRS. M: Mine stamp their feet.

Mrs. C: Mine just won't eat or they throw up.

Therapist: It sounds as though in some situations we and our children behave pretty much alike. *(All laugh.)*

As can be seen from the above excerpts, the group at this time was becoming quite mobile; exchanges between members were occurring somewhat more freely; and the general atmosphere was an easier and more permissive one. For some time, however, after the others began to loosen up, Mrs. M adhered closely to her earlier behavior. If she was starting to say something and another woman broke in, she would immediately stop. She practically never interrupted another member. When talking with another client, her voice would sometimes become louder, but in her exchanges with the therapist, she retained the whispering, subdued, submissive voice. This was something like her role in relation to her husband where her feelings were largely expressed symptomatically in her gastrointestinal disturbances, her insomnia, and the striking back at her husband through the provocation of her son. But now, with the encouragement of the permissive atmosphere of the group, Mrs. M seemed to be getting ready to move on.

In a discussion during the following session, when the group was talking about why children have to lie or deceive, Mrs. M suddenly asked, "Just how can you instil confidence into a child?" She said sometimes she felt confident and then would lose the feeling. Other members of the group chimed in, saying all children would be confident if it were not for the things that happen to them and destroy their confidence. In later sessions, Mrs. M recalled the days of her early youth when she, too, faced life more confidently. She recalled all the "nice little things my mother did for me," but now it was the women in the group who began doing things for her. Mrs. B, who prepared the group's coffee at the meetings (and who always remembered Mrs. M liked hers especially strong), tried to help in offering practical suggestions for the solution of Fred's school difficulties, and others supported Mrs. M in her feelings of resentment toward her husband.

Along with Mrs. M's changing role in the group, some changes became noticeable in her relationship to the therapist. At first, the changes—which were noted chiefly by the observer behind the one-way screen—were in her conversations with the other women before the group sessions began and when the therapist was not present. She would make a joke or a grimace when the therapist was out of the room and, at such times, she talked much more loudly than when he was present. Gradually, these freer attitudes were carried over into the sessions themselves. She abandoned her air of respectful submission toward the therapist, no longer followed his every word and even occasionally disagreed with him. When some of the other members of the group spoke of feeling exploited because they were women, Mrs. M agreed wholeheartedly.

In a session that took place almost six months after her introduction into the group, there was some intimation that these changes were altering her behavior within the family circle.

MRS. M: I came home the other day and my husband raised a terrible fuss because I'd been gone for three hours to visit a sick friend. I took my little girl with me, but I did not tell my husband where I was going. He probably would not have wanted me to go. When I came home, he began screaming and yelling and called me every name imaginable. He said all kinds of crazy things about what I had been doing.

Therapist: You mean he voiced all kinds of suspicions?

MRS. M: He goes out all the time, any time he pleases, any time he wants.

Therapist: You think that's why he's so furious when you go out?

MRS. M: He says he is going out. He gives no explanation. I used to yell when he would do things like that, but I found out it was no use because I was always the one to get hurt.

Mrs. B: It is sort of like your husband is sick. You do not know whether to give him a chance or not.

110

MRS. M: He used to go out all the time. He would just say he was going to the movies.

Mrs. B: My husband never used to do anything like that. If he did, I would have left him right away. (*The group laughs.*)

Therapist: Mrs. M said she used to get mad, but in ways that mostly hurt herself. Now if I understand her correctly, she is saying that she doesn't permit herself to get hurt so much.

Mrs. B: Maybe she can tell him before he starts to go out.

Therapist: You mean that perhaps in the past she has been too tolerant?

MRS. M: For quite a while I was.

Mrs. B: I would get so mad at my husband if he . . .

MRS. M: It is different now. Now I behave like my husband used to behave to me. I don't care so much any more, and I think that's what makes him so mad.

There could be little doubt that these changes in Mrs. M were making her husband very mad indeed, but surprisingly Mrs. M began to show a remarkable capacity to stand up to him. She reported to the group that not only did she refuse to let him bully her but that she would not permit him to bully the children either. This must have provoked some fearful scenes in the house, and Mrs. M admitted that it was sometimes hard on the children. However, Fred seemed to be deriving some real sense of security within his family for the first time. He told his mother that he was sure now that she loved him and that even if he had to leave the home, he would know that he had someone to whom he could come back.

It was after this that Fred was able, for the first time, really to participate with his therapist in a discussion of placement. It was possible for the mother and boy to discuss placement realistically together; and through the stressful months that followed, the boy was able to maintain a consistently positive attitude toward the plan. Although he was aware of his father's rejection, his growing relationship with his mother served to safeguard his sense of security. The boy and his mother made a visit together to the institution in which he was to be placed; and when final arrangements were ready to be made, Mrs. M brought the father into the procedure in a remarkably effective fashion.

In evaluating the contribution of the therapy group in this case, it is important to recall that it was not the sole therapeutic agent. Fred was helped considerably in the course of individual treatment,

111

and Mrs. M herself had derived some help in her treatment prior to her admission into the group. Mrs. M was included in the group, not because she had failed to make progress in individual treatment but rather because, as she progressed toward Fred's placement, she seemed unable to provide him with protection sufficient for the successful carrying through of the plan. Apparently the other women in the therapy group provided a kind of support not accessible to her in the individual treatment situation. With this support she was able to take a more effective role in Fred's placement and within the family circle as well.

VII. Use of Groups in the Intake Process

OUR FIRST THERAPY GROUPS were set up largely for those clients who had failed to make constructive use of individual treatment. The response of the clients suggested that a number of them might have profited by a therapy group experience at the very outset of contact, had it been available at the time. We found, in reviewing the intake interviews, that even then there were factors indicating that we would ultimately reach a therapeutic impasse. An obvious next step, therefore, was to try to adapt and utilize the therapy group in the intake process itself.

The purpose of intake in most agencies is to provide a means for the client and the agency to determine whether they can work together in the interest of the client's betterment. Through the intake process the worker has the opportunity to learn something of the nature of the client's problems, to evaluate the client's ability to use help, and to engage him in a therapeutic relationship. It also provides an opportunity for the client to explore his own difficulties and needs and to decide whether or not he wishes to make use of the services offered by the agency. In an agency serving delinquents, however, a number of factors operate to limit the client's freedom of choice. Even in an agency that is non-authoritarian and accepts only cases where the client wishes to engage in treatment "voluntarily," the worker should be aware

113

that these adolescents or parents usually do not seek help unless they are under some strong external pressure from the school, neighbors, relatives, or community. These coercive forces continue to operate to a greater or less degree no matter how explicit the intake worker may be in explaining to the client that he is under no compulsion to utilize treatment services. This sense of coercion not only tends to complicate the client's decision to accept treatment but also influences his total behavior in the intake interview, tending to obscure his true feelings. In consequence, the initial diagnostic impression may not be a valid one. This coercive factor, therefore, places limits on both the client and the worker in utilizing the intake situation as a starting point for the initiation of any kind of treatment.

At the clinic, we decided to set up intake groups to explore their possible value in facilitating three aspects of the intake process:

1. As a means of securing supplementary diagnostic data that are not readily accessible in individual intake interviews

2. As a means of providing both agency and client with a realistic base on which to decide the question of future treatment

3. As a means of involving the client in a therapeutic experience, in order that he might later utilize either individual treatment or some adaptation of group therapy.

Our previous experience with group therapy at the clinic had led us to believe that the group process might be an invaluable aid in all three of these intake purposes. For example, we found in our first group therapy project that significant alterations in the whole demeanor of certain "difficult" adolescents took place following their transfer from individual to group treatment. Their resistances, which were intimately related to their attitudes toward authority, were strongly mobilized in individual treatment but tended to relax in the less threatening atmosphere of the group. Also, this more permissive setting seemed to result in greater realism in accepting the need for treatment and in more active involvement in the treatment process itself.

It might be added that the spontaneous behavior of the adolescents at the clinic—such as the whispered conversations in the waiting-room and the corridors—served as an added stimulus to test

114

the potentials of a formalized group process. As they congregated in the hall they could be heard to ask what the other fellow was in for . . . what the tests meant . . . how long they would have to come . . . if it was better or worse to be seen by the clinic or the probation officer . . . or what they did to you if they decided you were crazy. We recognized that behind such questions lay a welter of feelings which, for the most part, were hidden and camouflaged the moment the adolescent entered the intake worker's office. It seemed to us that if such material could be made even partially accessible to discussion in a group setting, with a therapist participating, we might greatly increase the effectiveness of the intake process.

The selection and grouping of the adolescents for the first intake groups were done in rather rough fashion, particularly as compared with the painstaking care that had gone into planning the first group for continuing treatment. The adolescents admitted to an intake group generally fell within a two-year age range (usually 12 to 14 or 14 to 16). On the basis of the diagnostic information available at the time, we attempted to avoid overweighting the groups with youngsters who appeared to be psychopathic. Although little knowledge of personality patterns of the parents was available at the time the parent groups were set up, we considered it advisable to avoid overweighting the groups with parents who seemed rejecting of their children or who strongly favored their placement. Specifically excluded were both adolescents and parents whose particular situations seemed so complex or overwhelming that they appeared to require careful individual study from the outset.

The meeting place of these intake groups was generally in the therapist's office. As with the other groups, refreshments were usually served and the over-all atmosphere was made as informal as possible. The methodology had to be evolved as practice progressed. For instance, one device, which has been used in various ways, was first introduced fortuitously. A continuing therapy group which had met several times chanced to be meeting next door to an intake group having its second session. When one of the members of the older group went to the icebox to fetch the cokes he discovered that there was more than the usual supply.

When he reported this to his group, the therapist explained that a group of new boys was meeting next door and that refreshments had been supplied for all. First the group thought it would be a good idea to confiscate the entire loot, but after some discussion decided to give the others a break, and even "a little service" by taking cokes to them. The therapist of the intake group encouraged the boy who brought in the cokes to remain for a while and to help answer the new boys' questions. The "old timer," in his incisive replies, touched on several points that were of major concern to the group. He assured them of the confidentiality of the material and of the trustworthiness of the therapist. He told them that they would not be prodded into talking but that the responsibility for their participation would rest primarily on them. He succeeded in conveying to the new boys some of his own positive feelings and attitudes about the clinic in a way that was both meaningful and acceptable to them. It was better than any device that could conceivably have been introduced by the therapist himself.

Subsequently, on a planned basis, one or several new clients have been introduced into some groups that have been meeting for some time and, conversely, clients who have been in a treatment group for some time have been included in a newly-formed intake group. Such intermingling frequently offers many advantages to both the old and the new clients.

The following three excerpts from the clinic's records are presented to illustrate the use of the group to facilitate the three aspects of the intake process. Although these aspects obviously cannot be isolated from one another, we shall present each under the heading that it seems to illustrate best.[1]

Securing Supplementary Diagnostic Data

Leslie H, 14, was brought to court on a charge of engaging in homosexual activity. The probation officer's report described him as a rather isolated boy who did not participate in organized

---

[1] The examples cited here are drawn chiefly from groups conducted by three members of the staff, all of whom contributed substantially to the evaluation and description of the material presented in this section. They are Mrs. Bessie Ford, Kenneth Murase, and Victor De Santi.

116

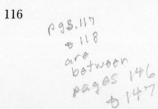

of the questions they had been asked previously at the clinic and court.

> Leslie: I don't want them to start asking me any more questions.
> Harry: They get you nervous, they keep on talking until you don't know what to say. My father told me I was coming down here to see about camp. He knew I wouldn't have come otherwise.
> Leslie: Why not?
> Harry: I don't like doctors. If I knew I had to see a doctor I wouldn't have come.

The group then engaged in a long discussion of what the clinic is and what doctors do. At the end of the session, however, Harry still maintained his point of view about medical men although the tenor of Leslie's remarks had somewhat changed.

> Harry: I have run away from other doctors. I would run away from the court.
> Therapist: Why do you run away?
> Harry: I just don't like doctors.
> Leslie: A doctor's job is to help you. Maybe some other doctor did something to hurt you.
> Harry: No, I don't know.

Throughout the session Harry continued to reject doctors, the clinic, and help in general, but he also rejected the support of his contemporaries. He was unable to accept the attempts at reassurance which were made by other boys in the group. It therefore seemed unlikely that Harry would be able to tolerate exposure to a treatment situation, either group or individual. Hence, it was no surprise that when, at the end of the session, the question of those who wished to continue was raised, Harry definitely stated that he did not want to return to the group, but would prefer to see a probation officer.

It is doubtful whether Harry, in an individual intake interview, would have been free enough to make his position clear in so definite a manner. His decision, and that of other boys who reject offers of help, does not relieve the clinic of its responsibility to provide some type of treatment plan. An honest exploration of the possibility of treatment, however, gives the adolescents an opportunity to accept or reject the offer. If it is rejected, the clinic at least is spared the time which should be given to other clients and which often is wasted in pursuit of an unreachable client.

119

Involving the Client in Treatment

Mary J,[2] a very disturbed girl, had given birth to a baby a few weeks before her sixteenth birthday. She had incurred strong disapproval of her old-world parents, who would have preferred to handle the matter themselves had not the Society for Prevention of Cruelty to Children brought the case to court. Even though Mary recognized that an agency had interceded to protect her from her parents' punitive measures, she was exceedingly distrustful of the court. Following her interview with the clinic psychiatrist, she expressed her disbelief in the confidentiality of the interview, indicating that the judge might have access to the material. In this, and in other ways, she revealed marked anxiety about the prospect of treatment.

In the first session of the intake group, she participated in the discussion about whether it was possible to trust the clinic. She seemed to gain some reassurance from the relative freedom with which the other girls were able to express their doubts openly and she was thus encouraged to talk about her own concerns. Her first remark was: "I don't see how the clinic can help me but I don't know what to do. My job is bad. My home is bad and I don't want to stay there." She said she thought it might be best just to "forget all about my troubles." She seemed surprised when the therapist made no response to this statement. In the discussion that followed the worker made it clear that the choice of accepting help or not was one that the girls must make for themselves. After the session, Mary spoke to the worker and asked directly for help with her problems. She explained that she wanted to gain custody of her baby. The worker gave her an appointment to discuss this question. Although it seemed evident that she would continue in individual sessions, she was given the opportunity of coming to the group once more.

Mary sat through the next session saying little. She did express relief that she was not the only one who had difficulties. Again she remained after the meeting to talk privately to the worker. She began to sob and told how unhappy she had been since losing both her boy friend and her baby. It seemed evident that Mary now

2 The individual treatment of Mary is described on pp. 42–45.

120

felt that the worker was allied with her. The therapy group doubtless had helped her move quickly from her former distrust to a position of seeking help and support. She made a revealing comment later, when she was defending her sexual relations with the father of the baby, in an interview with her worker. She quoted what one of the other girls in the group had said: "You've got to get love from some place." She went on to explain that there had been no love for her at home: "I was nothing—only the tenth child."

Her own explanation of her need influenced our decision to select individual rather than group therapy for her. It was our impression, however, that this brief group experience as an introduction to the clinic and its aims greatly increased the girl's capacity to enter into a treatment relationship. Although she did not discuss her problems in any detail in the group, she seemed to lose some of her hopelessness when she found her kind of trouble was not unique. She gained some security as she was able to identify herself with the other girls and their difficulties. Also, the permissive atmosphere of the group helped her realize that the process of accepting help would not thrust her into the passive role that had been forced upon her by her family. The fact that she was able spontaneously to approach the therapist at the end of the two sessions promised well for an active participating role in a treatment relationship.

Summary

Follow-up studies of our intake groups indicate that the use of the group process contributes significantly to the development of a productive treatment relationship. The intake group, either as the major or as a supplementary procedure, appears to be helpful in the following ways:

1. Intake groups give the workers an opportunity to observe clients in a setting that makes available important supplementary diagnostic data. These additional data serve as an aid in elaborating the diagnostic picture and in deepening our understanding of the total situation that brought the child or the parents to the court. Although certain dangers are inherent in relying on intake groups

as the sole instrument for collecting clinical data, we found that group interaction does make accessible certain types of information—especially responses that reveal strengths and assets—which often are obscured, because of strong resistances, in the individual intake interview.

2. The meeting of the worker and the client in the group situation enables them to relate to each other in a more productive and meaningful way than is possible in the individual interview. The presence of the client's peers enables the client, whether child or parent, to correct his distortions about treatment and to make his decision about becoming involved in a relationship on a more valid basis than would otherwise be possible.

3. The changes that take place in the client's feelings in even a few group sessions seem to lead to a more productive use of treatment services, whether the ultimate plan calls for continuance of group or individual treatment, or for referral to another agency.

Although the techniques employed in the intake groups at the clinic are not identical with the techniques employed in continuing therapy groups, they both are adaptations of the group psychotherapy method. The modifications of procedures were designed to meet the particular needs of the clients in this setting. It is our opinion that the application of group therapy techniques may prove useful to other agencies and institutions, not only in continuing treatment but also in the difficult task of initiating and consolidating a therapeutic relationship.

VIII. Group Therapy as the Sole Procedure

WHETHER GROUP THERAPY ALONE is an adequate treatment procedure for delinquents is a question that cannot be categorically answered. As we developed our clinic program, we found that a number of the delinquents, as well as their parents, seemed to make considerable progress in the intake groups. We decided, therefore, to offer only group therapy to a few clients who seemed, on the basis of certain rough diagnostic criteria, to be able to utilize the group experience productively. Our criteria were chiefly the absence of acute mental illness and the apparent diminution of resistance in the group setting.

In some instances we transferred a client from an intake group to an existing treatment group. In other instances, we used the intake group itself—after it had held two to four sessions—to form the nucleus of a continuing therapy group; some of the original members were transferred to other services and new members were added, usually from other intake groups. Effort was made to draw in new members who would aid in establishing a proper balance.

A number of cases, including both parents and children, received only group therapy throughout their clinic contact. We are of the opinion that where this procedure was relevantly employed, good results were obtained. We found, however, that this single-treatment approach did not seem indicated for many clinic cases. Obviously the criteria for the selection of cases for such treatment need to be further developed.

One case will be presented to illustrate the use of the group approach: Both the mother, Mrs. Foster, and her daughter, Florence, were members of continuing treatment groups.

FLORENCE FOSTER

Florence, age 14, was the eldest of four children, who all lived at home with their parents. She was brought to the court because she had set fire to some work materials in the classroom. The information available at the time of the clinic intake included the probation officer's investigation and a psychiatric and psychological examination. From these data, it appeared that her parents, especially her father, were extremely strict. Florence had few friends, was forbidden to leave the street on which she lived, and was not permitted to attend church dances although friends and relatives did so. The mother often kept her home from school to help with household chores or to take care of the younger children. The mother was described as a passive, ineffectual person who appeared to be completely dominated by her husband. She said that even when she did not fully agree with his methods, she felt that she had no alternative but to carry out the rigid disciplinary measures he imposed.

Florence seemed meek and made a drab appearance. She was not permitted to use make-up and her hair showed no evidence of care. She was not allowed to wear the casual shirts and dungarees worn by most girls in her age group. Her entire appearance seemed designed to produce an effect of complete neutrality. In contacts with the probation officers, judge, and psychiatrist she was entirely conforming, answering questions when asked, but was obviously attempting to withdraw as much as possible from them.

There was evidence of some tension during the psychiatric examination and several times she appeared on the verge of tears. On the psychological examination she scored an I.Q. of 85 on the full scale; 89 on performance and 84 on the verbal scales. She paid little attention to detail and it was difficult to obtain her sustained interest or attention. She became easily confused in working through logical relationships. She was retarded on the achievement tests and scored only at the fourth- or fifth-grade level in the school achievement tests. In all these contacts—and later when on one or two occasions she was alone with the group therapist during the early months of her treatment—she seemed extremely uncomfortable, restless, and withdrawn.

Florence was included in an intake group of seven girls in the 14-16 age range which was conducted by a female therapist. The mother was placed in a parents' intake group conducted by a male therapist. During the first session Florence's behavior appeared to confirm the impressions of the psychiatrist, who had described her as "isolated." Florence, however, also revealed briefly some of the feelings underlying her withdrawal and outward conformity. In the course of the discussion, the girls had raised questions about the relationship of the clinic to the court and the nature of their visits to the clinic.

> Evelyn: Will we have to tell you everything that happened to us?
> Therapist: Would that be hard?
> FLORENCE: It sure would be hard.
> Therapist: Of course, unless you wish to talk about these things, we won't go very far. I wonder if some of you have any idea about whether you must come here? Do any of you know about that?
> FLORENCE: I don't know.
> Marion: Of course you have to come.
> Therapist: Is that the way the rest of you understand it? Can you be forced to come?
> FLORENCE: Well, maybe a person just couldn't come. If you made them come, maybe they wouldn't come anyway.
> Therapist: What do you think the court would do then?
> Evelyn: They would get mad.
> FLORENCE: They would keep after you and they would ask, "Well, when can you come?"

From this brief excerpt, we could sense Florence's feelings about the court as another coercive force in her life and could anticipate that she would steel herself to resist it. Even in the group, however, she seldom revealed these feelings. She attended sessions regularly and evidenced continuing conformity. She was exposed to the continuous provocation and stimulation of girls who were all less conforming than Florence. In the second session, the girls were discussing the basis on which they had been referred to the clinic and why they had been brought to the attention of the court.

Beatrice: My probation officer told me she was sending me here because she had no time to see me.
Therapist: Well, that might be one of the reasons.
Beatrice: She didn't even tell me how long I would be on probation.
Celeste: Mine told me she didn't want to see me.
Marion: Mine told me I was so nervous they would send me to the clinic.
Phyllis: I guess they thought I was crazy because they gave me all those tests. I don't see what the judge or the court has to do with me.
Celeste: The court told my mother, "You have no jurisdiction over the girl. She is in our hands." Now she won't even let me go to the park.
Phyllis: If your mother doesn't mind your going out I don't see anything wrong with it. If your mother trusts you, I don't see why the court can't trust you.
Celeste: They [the court] think just because we are in a park we do all kinds of nasty things.
Therapist: What do you mean, nasty things?
Celeste: They think there is a couple under every bush. I was at the beach the other day and I was talking to a cop, and I said, "What do they keep you here for?" And he said they have to put a report into the police station of the names of girls who are at the beach at night.

Phyllis, Marion, and Celeste then began talking about other girls who do such things but who don't get caught. The group began telling who had brought them to court.

Marion: With me, it was just a neighbor who thought her daughter was getting into trouble with me and called the cops.
Mildred: With me it was the school.
Therapist: How about the rest of you? (*looking in Florence's direction*)
FLORENCE: With me it was the fire marshal. (*The other girls look up in surprise and Florence half-whispers something to Celeste.*)
Celeste: Why, if I was in that school it *would* have burned down.
Phyllis: What did she do?
Celeste (*shouting with laughter*): She tried to burn down the school.

The rest of the girls laughed loudly. Florence grinned sheepishly, but with a suggestion of bravado. It was not until some months later, however, that she began to express her feelings more openly. Although she obviously did not trust either the clinic or the therapist, she nevertheless continued to attend regularly. During a session in the fourth month of treatment, the therapist had occasion to refer to the confidentiality of the clinic records. Florence interrupted her to say: "Oh, I know that everything we do here you tell the probation officer." The remark was made in a bold, provocative manner. Later on in the session she jokingly referred to the attractiveness of the male therapist who was conducting the group attended by her mother, and she began to express direct concern and suspicion about what her mother might be saying in her group sessions. This single foray was not, however, immediately followed by any further similar demonstration.

In the few adventures in revealing her feelings that she did undertake, she usually beat a strategic withdrawal almost as soon as she had begun. For the most part, she talked rarely and was especially silent when some of the more aggressive girls were holding forth. When she did speak, she stayed close to subjects which she considered safe and with which she felt at home. These generally involved discussion of the relative merits of Joe DiMaggio or the standing of the various local baseball teams. Occasionally, she engaged in some mild bragging about some of her own athletic exploits. She tended to do this especially when the material under discussion made her uncomfortable. Needless to say, such diversionary techniques on her part did not help win friends for her in the group.

> Celeste (to Phyllis): What time did you get home last night?
> Phyllis: Ten after 12.
> Mildred: You better watch your step or you will be seeing the judge again.
> FLORENCE: I am going to start doing some weight lifting.
> Celeste: What in God's name for?
> FLORENCE: Just for fun.
> Celeste: Fun! By the time you are 20 you are going to look like a man walking around. What in the world do you want muscles for?
> FLORENCE: Just for fun.
> Celeste (sarcastically): Well, I must say, at least it is a decent, good, healthy way to pass the time. You keep on lifting weights. I've got a girl friend around my way who does the same thing, but she is not right in the head anyway.

Florence was completely demolished by this assault and said relatively little during the remainder of the session. The group moved on, following other interests, leaving her somewhat outside their circle, a position she usually occupied during the early months of the group. Just at the point where we were starting to wonder whether our decision to place her in this group had been a correct one, we noticed a difference in the way she was beginning to operate in the group. Previously, she had withdrawn or tried to change the subject, as indicated above, whenever the material was related to

127

delinquent acts or when the other girls discussed their sexual activities.

In one session, after about three months of group treatment, the girls were talking of their various experiences with boy friends. They then expressed a great deal of feeling about a girl's disadvantages and the unfair things that boys could do to girls. They went on to voice considerable resentment at the humiliation they had felt at the way these matters had been handled by the court. During the discussion, Florence unmistakably displayed interest. Instead of sitting slumped back in her chair, she was practically on the edge of her seat and listening and watching the other girls intently. However, she said little except almost casually to mention that she had recently taken a walk late at night through a neighborhood where girls were known to have been attacked. She described with some relish the anxiety her parents had shown when they had heard about it.

At the next session, Florence, who heretofore had always dressed so drably, appeared with a heavy application of lipstick and brilliant red nail polish. For the first time, she spoke of her own feelings about and interest in boys. In subsequent sessions, as her participation increased, Florence was able to win some acceptance from the group members. They would occasionally laugh with her rather than at her—even when she told a story of losing her shorts at a basketball game. A moment of real triumph occurred when she and and another member of the group, both of whom were ardent basketball fans, took over the session on the day that a local college basketball team won a national championship, and the students demonstrated on the streets outside of the clinic. Florence's close identification with so world-shaking an event seemed to help her achieve full status in the group.

Although Florence continued to be the object of occasional "ribbing" by the rest of the girls, who still referred to her as the "sweet and innocent type," she was more or less able to hold her own with them. This would not have been possible without the support, protection, and encouragement of the therapist. It was obvious that she did derive sustenance from such support, but she nevertheless was silent and uncomfortable with the therapist

128

on the occasions that she found herself alone with her, such as when Florence happened to arrive early. In the group she seemed less tense even though she was exposed to the joking and taunting comments of the girls.

During this phase, Florence's position in the group reflected her basic psychological problem: she was suspicious and distrustful of adults, including her parents, teachers, and the therapist, but at the same time she had to maintain an outwardly conforming attitude toward them in order to conceal these hostile feelings. Her hostility gave rise to such symptomatic behavior as her silences and withdrawal from the group. Her relationships with her contemporaries were hardly more satisfactory. The pattern of withdrawal, which had served as a necessary defense for such a long time, impeded the establishment of satisfactory ties with her peers. She, therefore, was not able, like most adolescents, to work out in a healthy manner, by identification with youngsters of her own age, the problems that had been incompletely resolved within the family circle.

In the therapy group, where she was somewhat shielded from attack and rejection by the girls, she was slowly able to win a place for herself with them. Only when she sensed their acceptance could she begin to acknowledge some of her long-repressed feelings about her parents and other adults. In these efforts she was provoked and encouraged, of course, by the members of the group who were less inhibited in expressing negative feelings. They thus acted as "instigators" [3] for Florence.

Had this process taken place in a setting other than a therapy group, it is quite possible that it would have been accompanied by an intensification of the delinquent behavior. Even with the controls of a therapy group, there is a danger that the members may act out their hostility as the repressive forces are relaxed. Florence at this point began to talk with great familiarity about questionable happenings in her neighborhood, such as car thefts, gang fights, and so on. She usually told stories in the third person but her intimate knowledge of these affairs made us wonder whether she might be participating in them. She spoke with gleeful apprecia-

[3] Term used by S. R. Slavson, *An Introduction to Group Therapy*, The Commonwealth Fund, New York, 1943, p. 119.

tion of the "bad man" in a gangster movie. Once, with obvious delight, she told about a girl who had thrown an eraser at her teacher.

After about six months of treatment, Florence began to drop this kind of indirection and to manifest many hostile impulses of her own. She joined with the others in attacking the court, school authorities, the police, and the moral standards of the community. She spoke disparagingly of the clinic and became openly hostile and provocative toward the therapist. When these tactics failed to elicit a punitive response, she seemed able to move foward and express some of her deep feelings of resentment against her parents. She told of an unendurable conflict she had always experienced, since they both used her as a pawn in their battles with each other.

> Phyllis: Let me tell you what I did the other morning. I wanted to wear my socks to school but my mother made me let my little sister wear them. She said that they were her socks and then my brother got into the fight so I just took some coffee and threw it at my mother, every bit of it.
> Evelyn: I should have been there.
> Phyllis: My mother said you are this and you are that. I said I would call Mrs. B [the therapist]. Everybody takes advantage of me. . . . I feel like I am going crazy. It is the house I live in.
> Marion: Maybe it is the building.
> Phyllis: I just can't stand that house.
> Therapist: What do you mean?
> Phyllis: As long as I am doing something it doesn't bother me. When I sit down I feel crazy-like.
> Marion: You feel crazy? You are crazy!
> FLORENCE: I know what she means. The other day I was by the sink in the kitchen and my mother was in the bathroom. I just couldn't help saying, "You dirty double-crossing rat." My mother said, "What was that?" I just don't know why I did it.
> Marion: When everybody is talking at once I could just grab and hold them and shake them to death and when they don't stop, I want to scream.
> Phyllis: My mother treats me like the footstool of a queen. I can't go to the movies with my girl friend. She says, "You know you are not going to the show with no girl. You are going with a boy. You are going this place and that place," and I say, "Never mind, I don't want to go anyway."
> Therapist: Phyllis is really having a tough time.
> Phyllis: When I ask for money my uncle gives me money.
> FLORENCE: When I ask my father for money he says, "Ask your mother," and when I ask my mother she says, "Ask your father."
> Therapist: So you are in between.

FLORENCE: My father never gives me any money when I ask him.

Phyllis: I can't help it if I am not like other kids. I am not treated like other kids. The best thing I can do is cry it out. Before I go to school I have an argument with everybody in the house. The only one I get along with is my little sister.

FLORENCE: It's Hallowe'en and all the kids are home from school and just because everybody is out on the street I can't go out but if nobody is out then they let me go out.

Phyllis: I ask my mother if I could go out for about an hour and a half. She says no, she is going out.

FLORENCE: One night I really got mad. I was talking to my mother and I got so mad I said I was going to run away so she just put on her coat and said, "Come on." I said, "Where are we going?" and she said, "To the police station," and then I got scared so I asked for 20 cents. She thought I would run away with 20 cents but I told her I just wanted to go to the store. She made me go with a girl friend and she stood on the stoop watching me.

Phyllis: Do you think 11:30 is too late to be out on a Saturday night?

FLORENCE: Friday nights I go to a school dance with the kids and my mother makes me be home by 11:30. It is only with my father that I don't have any trouble.

Therapist: What do you mean, trouble?

FLORENCE: I like my father to give me things but when I ask him he says, "Ask your mother." He promised to give me 70 cents to go to the show but when I asked him for it on Sunday he said, "Go get it off your mother." When my mother says she doesn't have any he hollers at her and says, "What do you do with your money?"

Therapist: It doesn't seem fair to you?

Phyllis: Sure, my mother's boy friend is fairer to me than she or my brother is.

FLORENCE: My brother gets away with murder. He doesn't come home until 9 P. M. but I can't do anything.

Phyllis: My brother comes home at 12. My mother won't let me go out to a party unless my brother goes. To tell the truth my brother's friends treat me better than my brother does. If it wasn't for them I would always be lonely.

FLORENCE: Whenever I bring kids into the house the superintendent is always complaining that we are running in and out. He always causes trouble. They believe everybody but no one ever believes me.

In this session, Florence revealed her deep sense of hurt at the hands of her parents and her awareness that she was caught in the middle of their long-standing conflict. The father had not only forced Florence to conform to his wishes, but he also had engendered in her tremendous guilt and anxiety by pitting her against her mother.

As will be seen in the report of the mother's activity in the parents' group (presented later), Florence's movement in treatment was beginning to be reflected in her behavior at home. Fortunately the mother had made sufficient progress in her group treatment so that she was increasingly able to tolerate some of these rather startling changes. (Note the discussion about Florence's smoking cigarettes.) [4] Had this not been the case, Florence's progress might have resulted in more conflict with her family, and perhaps ultimately have had negative effects on her over-all life situation.

Certain further changes in Florence's relationship to the therapist now took place. For example, she was able to smoke in the group without expressing her concern, as she had done previously, that the therapist would "squeal" on her. She seemed more at ease in her attitudes toward the clinic itself; on one occasion she brought a friend as a guest. Also, she began to take the lead in the group's discussions. One day she told of a boat trip that she had taken over the holidays, noting especially that there were boys and girls on the trip. She spoke of flirting with some of the boys. She said that on the way they had passed the girls' detention center where she had stayed at the time when she was first brought into court, implying that this part of her life was all over now. She reported that she was trying to "pull up" her school grades so that she would be able to graduate and go on to high school in the fall. She also said she hoped that she would not have to be at the clinic at that time since she would prefer that the high school not know about her court experience. Florence, whose tests had placed her at the dull normal level of intelligence, succeeded in finishing the eighth grade and entered high school.

She was discharged from the clinic several months after her graduation from the elementary school. She had had more than a year and a half of treatment.

Mrs. Foster

At the time of the clinic's initial contact with the F family, the psychiatrist who made the diagnostic examination noted that he thought Florence could be helped by psychiatric treatment provided that the attitudes of both parents underwent some change.

[4] See p. 136.

As is often the case, the father's hours of employment made it impractical for him to come to the clinic on a regular basis. We decided, therefore, that we would undertake to establish a contact with the mother through the medium of group therapy, and see what might be accomplished by the dual treatment of mother and child.

Mrs. F was described by the psychiatrist as "a rather passive, inadequate individual completely under her husband's domination. . . . She realizes that he is very strict with the girl but is afraid to do anything about it and . . . she carries out her husband's commands without question." Mrs. F reported a history of hypertension and of poliomyelitis as a child. She also mentioned an occasional "weakness" of one leg which seemed to trouble her especially at times of stress.

Obviously, an attempt to change the "attitudes" of Mrs. F was hardly a simple task, nor was there any assurance that any progress that might be achieved with her would necessarily better the daughter's situation. Our doubts about a successful outcome in this case were based on previous unproductive efforts to treat a relatively submissive mother and child while nothing was done to change the dominant, autocratic father. In this case, we might well expect considerable resistance on the part of the mother to changes in the child. Such resistance generally is designed to protect the parent from the additional stresses precipitated by alterations in the family equilibrium which occur when the child's behavior begins to change. To overcome such resistance is difficult and may even be unwise if the parent cannot be provided with the necessary support and protection. Our previous experience with therapy groups had demonstrated the usefulness of the group in resolving this sort of problem, and in providing certain supports.

In her first session, Mrs. F was considerably more verbal than Florence had been in hers. Florence had been withdrawn and had remained almost literally outside the group. But Mrs. F, too, in spite of ability to speak in the group, tried to isolate and conceal herself. As shown below, she made clear at the opening of her first session her intention to remain uninvolved.

Therapist: Well, as I suggested in my letter to you, since your children come to the clinic, we think that we should have the opportunity of talking with you, too.

133

MRS. F: It is no use, you can't get through to them, and as for us, we can do this and we can do that but it does no good. So far as I am concerned, I am staying in my own corner. I will try to trust my daughter and leave it up to her.

Therapist: Well, here at the clinic we feel that, although children come here for help, that by talking it over with you—

MRS. F *(interrupting)*: You want to hear both sides? Well, I guess that's all right, but we don't *have* to come down here. *I* came anyway because—

Mrs. G *(laughing)*: Yes, that's right, it isn't easy sometimes. I'm telling you. . . .

MRS. F: I suppose it is all right if you are not too strict, but my husband is too strict with my daughter. She wants to go to shows and P. A. L. [Police Athletic League] dances. My husband is dead set against it. He said that if she doesn't come home tonight there is going to be trouble. You are right, it isn't easy.

Mrs. G: Yes, it is that way with my daughter, too.

MRS. F: She tells me, "I don't have to wash the dishes." It's the attitude that gets me. "I'll fix you this morning," I said. I asked her to walk across the street to the candy store for me, and she says "I don't want to go for you." She snaps at you like that. She doesn't care.

Therapist: Well, this is the sort of thing we thought we might get together and talk about. What do you think?

Mrs. H: I think it's a good idea. My kid is just like Mrs. Foster's. If I tell my kid to do something he says "just a minute."

Mrs. G: My daughter is the same way.

MRS. F: The doctor said my husband was too strict with her. As for me, I would let her go to the dances. I would let her stay out until 12 o'clock. I don't care.

Therapist: You are saying perhaps that you feel the clinic tells your child she can do as she pleases?

MRS. F: I can't see why my daughter does these things.

Mrs. G: With my husband I won't let him raise a hand to the girl. He doesn't dare hit her.

MRS. F: If I don't have the food on the table when my husband wants it, that's too bad. I have to keep everything from him. Right now I am in such a fuddle between him and going twice a day to the hospital to see my mother I just wish I could get away to some place in the country.

Mrs. F's expressed wish to stay in her "corner" was a clear warning that she wished to evade involvement in treatment. She also in-dicated that she was concerned about the permissive attitudes of the clinic and about their possible disturbing effect on both her daughter and herself. She first related her concern about greater freedom to her fear of her strict husband. Later, however, she related her concern to herself and her own family background.

The parents were talking about various recreational centers:

MRS. F: There is no place to play. Even the parents get into difficulties with people in the neighborhood. My girl doesn't have any one to play with. She has to hold everything inside. The children all pick on her.

Mrs. H: When my son came home [from the detention center] for two weeks nobody in the neighborhood would even talk to him. Everybody took the attitude that he was a criminal, so he kept away from everybody.

MRS. F: That's what the judge and doctor explained. They hold everything inside. . . . I don't know, I do something for her birthday every year. . . . It was different with me and my mother when I was a girl. She was always picking on me. The way I was raised it was "do it or else." I drove my mother crazy.

The group supported Mrs. F in her feelings of resentment against Florence and, when Mrs. F expressed the wish to send her away to camp, they obviously were in sympathy with her feelings. Mrs. F responded to their agreement by making a surprising about-face.

MRS. F: Well, it's no use. In the next three years she will have to face things anyway. Running away doesn't help; it's no good. Something inside has to come out. After all, she didn't do anything that was too bad.

This statement had an entirely different quality from Mrs. F's initial remarks; she seemed now to be questioning a "running away" solution, either for herself or her daughter. Although this rather surprising reversal was only transient in nature, and could not be expected to effect any change in Mrs. F or in her role in the family at this time, the fact that she had this much mobility was itself a good prognostic omen. In spite of her marked resistance at the opening of the session, she was able, in response to the group, to reverse her position. The group succeeded in neutralizing her tendency to run away or give up, and even in stimulating her to think of her situation in less hopeless terms. This much movement, at the outset of treatment, suggests that the group experience provides the kind of support that some very resistive parents can use constructively.

Mrs. F's closing remarks at her first session illuminated her need for the group's support in her anticipated adventures in the dangerous wilds of treatment.

MRS. F: Well, my daughter takes care of her own clothes. The only trouble with her is that she wants more and more money for recreation.

135

Therapist: Money means many things to children, and disagreements over allowances often point to something else.

Mrs. G: My daughter wants to be a lady of leisure. She wants me to fix her breakfast and have her clothes ready. She just wants to come in and eat.

MRS. F: If only I could get my husband to chip in $1.50 it would be enough. I wish I could get him to come down here and you could talk to him. A mother's job is only part of it.

Mrs. G (*emphatically*): That's right. There are always two sides.

Mrs. F never did succeed in bringing her husband to the group, but she apparently was able to use some of the strength and support she was deriving from the sessions in her dealings with him. These alterations in Mrs. F's role in the family contributed considerably to the total treatment plan, especially when Florence became less conforming. Mrs. F soon began to display great concern about what was going on in the sessions her daughter attended.

Mrs. G: The trouble with the kids is that they are on the street too much. That is where they get all kinds of ideas.

MRS. F: Yes, it isn't just the housework, it's the ideas. They just have too much of everything now.

Therapist: You mean that you can't let them do everything but there are some things. . . .

MRS. F: You mean they ought to think for themselves. Last week when Florence came home from the clinic I asked what they talk about there. She said, "I am not supposed to tell you." I said, "What do you mean, I am not supposed to know about it? Don't worry, I will find out what you talk about." She is afraid I am going to check on her for being bad.

Mrs. L: My kid keeps things to himself, too.

MRS. F: The first time they get into trouble makes them feel they are always being picked on.

Mrs. L: Oh, I never remind him of it. But sometimes they take advantage of it.

MRS. F: You have to talk to them even though you are not supposed to punish them at all. They can come here [to the clinic] and talk about it.

Mrs. L: My kid loves to come here.

MRS. F: Yes, Florence gets a big kick out of it too. She told me that Mrs. B [the therapist] gives them cokes and cigarettes. She knows about the other children in the group. She told me about another girl who doesn't want to do housework either.

Mrs. F's difficulty in tolerating Florence's behavior was undoubtedly increased by the need to control her own hostile feelings toward her husband. The resulting tension might well have forced Mrs. F to oppose any change in Florence and to sabotage her

136

treatment. With the support of group help, however, Mrs. F was able to acknowledge and to respond positively to the evidences of growth in her daughter. As she achieved this, Mrs. F was then able to move toward an examination of her own concerns.

Mrs. G: Yes, my daughter wants to sleep until 10 o'clock and doesn't want to get up.

MRS. F: Sometimes it has to do with their friends. Somebody told me that my daughter has a friend who looks like 18. It gives her ideas.

Mrs. G: Yes, they all give each other ideas.

MRS. F: Mine is going to school with a girl who I thought was a nice girl. She was quiet in our house, but she told me different stories about her family. She said her mother and father were separated.

Therapist: You think that might have had something to do with the child's disturbance?

MRS. F: It would disturb a child's mind to think that her mother and father were going separate ways. . . .

Therapist: Yes, fathers do have a good deal to do with the situation too, don't they?

MRS. F: When my daughter got into trouble with this girl, my husband said to me, "It is all your fault. I told you not to let her play with the girl." My husband thinks all we have to do is keep pounding at them and keep after them.

Therapist: You worry a great deal.

MRS. F: Of course I worry. So many things can happen. If they are late, you don't know what to do. If they don't come home, you go crazy. . . . And now every one is picking on Florence. But my sister says there is nothing wrong with Florence.

Here, Mrs. F appeared to be reacting against her own rapid movement. Having progressed to the point where she was able to touch on the relationship between her marital difficulties and her daughter's delinquency, she became panicky and even wanted to deny that her daughter had any problems at all. At this critical juncture, the therapist helped to mobilize group support for Mrs. F.

Therapist: Why do you think we ask children to come down here?

(The entire group responded at once to such an extent that it was almost impossible to distinguish the voices on the sound track.)

MRS. F: I know you want to help them.

Mrs. L: Yes, it gets so you even have to watch the way you talk to them.

MRS. F: When Florence was a little child she was sick and she got better, and then she got sick again.

Mrs. L: Were you nervous when you were carrying the baby?

MRS. F: No, I didn't even know what was happening. . . . The trouble with

137

mothers is that they promise too much to kids. They say "I am going to do this or that," and they can't do it.

Mrs. G: If you promise something, do it. You must not forget about it and beatings don't help.

MRS. F: No, they are over so quickly they don't even feel it.

Therapist: Perhaps if we knew what was behind these kinds of behavior we might be able to handle it.

MRS. F: Another thing—they always want money and it isn't good if you can't give it to them. They want to know why they can't have it. They don't understand.

As Mrs. F went on in a similar vein during the next several sessions, she made it increasingly clear that her concern over her inability to give Florence money was closely associated with her feelings around her inability to extend love to her daughter. It also became apparent how closely Mrs. F identified Florence's problems with her own early experiences and deprivation.

Later, when Mrs. F began to think of her difficulties with her daughter less as the result of circumstances and more as the effects of family relationships, she talked less of Florence and focused more on her own problems. She began to explore her own personal concerns and her worries about her health.

MRS. F: With my daughter it is different. I will let her get her working papers when she is 16. I said, "When you are 18 you can do as you please."

Mrs. G: That's right. They get very independent, especially my daughter.

Mrs. L: Oh yes, they always change.

Mrs. G: They overcome it. They all have to go through it.

MRS. F: Well, I see every one else's children have the same trouble. I used to feel there wasn't another one made like my daughter. . . .

Mrs. G: That's right. My daughter is the same way.

MRS. F: Each child has his own way of working it out.

Mrs. G (*turning to Mrs. F*): How do you feel?

MRS. F: I feel pretty good. I have hot flashes now and then, but it isn't too bad now. I told you about it last time. The girl is becoming all right now, too. Now it is the rest of the family that is bothering me. I used to have both my mother and my brother-in-law in the house. Now it is some one else's turn. I had the doctor because I was sick and I explained about my mother. My sister cursed everybody in the house. I sat there and didn't say anything, and the next day I was sick. I was so weak I couldn't do anything for my mother. Oh, I can visit her and help her morale by making her feel good but I just can't take her into my house. I had her so long before and I did my best. But you just can't sit back and forget it.

Mrs. G: No, you can't.

MRS. F: Well, I am not having so much trouble with Florence any more.

Mrs. G: I am glad to hear it. . . . As for myself, it is getting worse every day.

MRS. F: What's the trouble?

Mrs. G: I tell her one thing and others tell her another thing. If I tell her not to go out she goes out anyway.

Mrs. H: What about your husband?

Mrs. G: I try to handle it myself and keep him out of it. He has such a hot temper. First thing you know he will hit her so I don't let him bother with her at all.

MRS. F: At the beginning I didn't let my husband bother with Florence. The other day there were two boys outside who were fist-fighting and using bad language. My stomach hurt me when I saw them. Florence was watching the boys fight, and my husband saw her and told her to get across the street. He asked her why she was watching and didn't she hear them using that language? "I am not listening to their language," she said, "I am watching them fight." He got mad and said, "Get into the house." She came in and cried but you couldn't get it through her head that she did anything wrong. I told her to go to the dance but she said that her father wouldn't let her. I said, "Go outside and I will get you to the dance, but next time you listen when you are told something." She was gone like a bullet. My husband says, "Where's Florence?" I said I let her go to the dance. That night my husband had an accident in his car. . . . He gets cranky when he has an accident. . . . If he comes home aggravated, and there are difficulties in the home, it is just like putting an atom bomb in the living room.

Mrs. G: That's right. A man doesn't understand how to handle the situation.

Mrs. H: They don't have the patience.

MRS. F: No, they don't. I tell my husband now, "I take care of my home. You take care of your job." Why now even when you ask the baby who is the boss in this family, the baby says, "Mommy is the boss."

It seems evident from this material that the forces that previously had driven Mrs. F into illness and had placed a great burden of conflict on her daughter were being successfully rechanneled.

Such changes in her feelings and in her role in the family obviously were essential to the successful treatment of her daughter, which was the clinic's major responsibility. But the gains seemed more extensive. A change in the relationship between the parents also took place, growing out of the efforts to improve the parent-child relationship. In an interview just prior to termination of treatment, Mrs. F pointed to considerable improvement in her relationship not only with Florence and the other children but with her husband as well. She recognized that she still had many problems, but she stated that she had learned to handle them better, and was no longer afraid of them. She said she had enjoyed the group tremendously and thought that she might perhaps visit it again sometime. She told with pride that she no longer was so concerned about the opinion of neighbors. Now she said, "I feel able to do what I think is right."

The therapist, in her report to the court recommending discharge —after a little more than a year of treatment—noted that "during her attendance at the parents' therapy group meetings, Mrs. F, through the support and acceptance she obtained from the group and the therapist, has become more flexible in handling her daughter's behavior. She has become less fearful of the steps that Florence has been taking toward adulthood. As a consequence, she can, for example, permit the girl to make some of her own plans about what she will do when she finishes school and give her more freedom in selecting her friends."

Mrs. F came to recognize that she, along with the other parents, had experienced deprivations that affected them as parents. As she was able to change certain aspects of her mode of functioning, and as she gained some insight into her ways of operating, she became less rigid and punishing in all her relationships. In spite of the many reality problems imposed by financial difficulties and physical illness, she was, with group support, enabled to abandon much of her somatic symptomatology.

At her last session at the clinic, Mrs. F, accompanied by Florence, made her formal farewells. Both she and her daughter displayed considerable assurance as they talked to the clinic staff. Several years after the completion of treatment, both were continuing to do well.

IX. Conclusion

NOTHING IS TO BE GAINED by oversimplifying the problems encountered in the extramural treatment of the adolescent delinquent and his parents. The technical problems are extremely difficult and they, in turn, are complicated by almost insuperable administrative ones. We have endeavored to set forth the problems we encountered in our work, and also to indicate some ways in which they might be successfully attacked.

We believe that workers who have truly integrated the basic psychiatric concepts in their experiences in other treatment areas will find much that is familiar in the central theories we have elaborated. A grasp of these basic principles is essential for effective work with the delinquent. But theoretical knowledge and classical treatment experience alone do not equip the worker for successful therapy with delinquents. The differences, as well as the similarities, between the problems of delinquents and of others must be understood by those who expect to work with the people who pass through our juvenile courts. The operations of such authoritative agencies as the police, the detention centers, and the courts themselves must be thoroughly understood before a worker is able to engage in treatment. Working with delinquents demands a continuous fusion of epidemiological and clinical understanding, diagnostic acumen, and administrative "know-how." To make a flat statement of this credo is easy. To find this combination of knowledge and skill embodied in any one mortal staff member is somewhat more difficult.) The administrator of an agency working with delinquents has to employ a task force that can encompass as much of this professional armamentarium as possible.

The existing treatment agencies, even if multiplied many times over, would hardly make an appreciable dent in the incidence of delinquency. Thus, if continued therapeutic activities in the field of delinquency are to be justified, it seems evident that responsibilities must be assumed that extend beyond the treatment of those children and parents who are referred to an agency or clinic after they have come into court. No single treatment agency, obviously, can undertake the multiple prophylactic measures which are more properly the job of the community as a whole. But any agency can give leadership to the community in developing preventive work and, in so doing, will also gain greater perspective about the place of its special activities within the context of the total community needs.

Since communities tend to use the courts and treatment agencies in lieu of developing the kinds of services which might lessen the need for such agencies, the treatment agency has an obligation to scrutinize and study its referrals with a view to identifying the groups of individuals who are being thrust toward delinquency because of breakdowns and deficiencies in certain community services. Psychotherapeutic services must not be jockeyed into the position of serving as a stop-gap for poorly functioning or inadequate social services and facilities. In some instances, an agency can productively invest some of the staff's time in assisting the community to make the extra effort—or add the technical skill or needed funds—to reach and provide resources for some part of the delinquent or pre-delinquent population. For example, many of the children and their families who pass through the courts would not appear there at all if schools developed programs that more nearly met the needs of the culturally and economically deprived children in the community. Increased facilities for scholastic, vocational, and personal counseling, as well as remedial education within the schools, would prevent many problems of maladjustment and would at the same time provide courts with resources to which they could refer cases that do not require either continuing super-

142

vision from an authoritative agency or the intensive treatment of a psychotherapeutic facility. In like manner, as community centers develop casework services or "detached" programs—working with delinquents in their own milieus—they should be able to achieve results not possible by agencies utilizing the more classical treat-ment methods. Family or children's agencies, if they develop group treatment programs and adopt a philosophy of "reaching out" to the suspicious and guarded people found in the families of delinquents, may also achieve success not hitherto thought possible with these groups.

Any community agency that is providing an extramural treat-ment program for delinquents and their families must periodically assess its efforts in the light of over-all community needs and services. Sometimes, for example, it may have to push actively for the development of such a facility as a residential treatment center, both to meet the real needs of a particular group, and also to con-serve its own resources for families who can profit from out-patient therapy.

The principles and procedures discussed in the foregoing chapters, obviously, cannot be automatically applied in other settings. Care-ful adaptation and modification of the techniques to meet the unique requirements of a particular setting are necessary if a sound program is to be evolved. Extensive research on many levels is required if the problems of delinquency are to be attacked in any substantial measure.

As communities across the country become increasingly aware of the nature of the problem of delinquency, and become further involved in the immense task of doing something about this great social discrepancy, it seems probable that common denominators will emerge; the unique factors, both in etiology and in treatment, should become increasingly clear.

Many of the techniques discussed in this volume are not fully developed nor are their potentials clearly perceived. Any agency working with delinquents and their families, however, has a pro-fessional responsibility to apply current knowledge of personality in new ways in an effort to develop more adequate individual and group treatment methods.

Standards for training for work in the field of delinquency

143

cannot as yet be formulated. Training on the job has a particular value but it must be based on sound professional education provided by law schools, schools of social work, training institutions for psychiatrists, and other graduate institutions. All professional education—whether for psychiatrist, psychologist, social worker, or probation officer—should increasingly take cognizance of the special requirements for practice in the field of delinquency. Only by increasing the knowledge and competence of all the professional persons who deal with the delinquent can leadership be developed in this important field of human endeavor.

BIBLIOGRAPHY

ACKERMAN, NATHAN W.: "Psychotherapy and 'Giving Love,'" *Psychiatry*, Vol. VII, No. 2 (1944), 129–137.

AICHHORN, AUGUST: *Wayward Youth*, Viking Press, New York, 1935.

BENDER, LAURETTA: "Genesis of Hostility in Children," *American Journal of Psychiatry*, Vol. CV, No. 4 (1948), 241–245.

———— AND WOLTMANN, ADOLF G.: "Play and Psychotherapy," *The Nervous Child*, Vol. I, No. 1 (1941–42), 17–42.

BETTELHEIM, BRUNO: *Love Is Not Enough*, The Free Press, Glencoe, Ill., 1950.

CUNNINGHAM, JAMES M.: "Psychiatric Case Work as an Epidemiological Tool," *American Journal of Orthopsychiatry*, Vol. XVIII, No. 4 (1948), 659–669.

DOLLARD, JOHN, ET AL.: *Frustration and Aggression*, Yale University Press, New Haven, 1939.

EISSLER, K. R.: "Ego-Psychological Implications of the Psychoanalytic Treatment of Delinquents," *The Psychoanalytic Study of the Child*, Vol. V, International Universities Press, New York, 1950, 97–121.

EISSLER, RUTH S.: "Scapegoats of Society," *Searchlights on Delinquency* (K. R. Eissler, ed.), International Universities Press, New York, 1949, 288–305.

FRAIBERG, SELMA: "Some Aspects of Casework with Children," *Social Casework*, Vol. XXXIII, Nos. 9 and 10 (1952), 374–381; 429–435.

GARDNER, GEORGE E.: "The Juvenile Court as a Child Care Institution," *Federal Probation*, Vol. XVI, No. 2 (1952), 8–12.

GITELSON, MAXWELL: case presentation and discussion in "Direct Psychotherapy in Adolescence: Symposium, 1941," *American Journal of Orthopsychiatry*, Vol. XII, No. 1 (1942), 1–25.

GLUECK, SHELDON AND ELEANOR T.: *Unraveling Juvenile Delinquency*, Commonwealth Fund, New York, 1950.

GREENACRE, PHYLLIS: "Conscience in the Psychopath," *American Journal of Orthopsychiatry*, Vol. XV, No. 3 (1945), 495–509.

HACKER, FREDERICK J., AND GELEERD, ELISABETH R.: "Freedom and Authority in Adolescence," *American Journal of Orthopsychiatry*, Vol. XV, No. 4 (1945), 621–630.

HALLIDAY, JAMES L.: *Psychosocial Medicine: A Study of the Sick Society*, W. W. Norton & Co., New York, 1948.

HAMILTON, GORDON: *Psychotherapy in Child Guidance*, Columbia University Press, New York, 1947.

HEALY, WILLIAM, AND BRONNER, AUGUSTA F.: *New Light on Delinquency and Its Treatment*, Yale University Press, New Haven, 1936.

JENKINS, R. L.: "The Psychopathic Delinquent," *Social Work in the Current Scene:* Selected Papers, 76th Annual Meeting National Conference of Social Work, 1949, Columbia University Press, New York, 1950, 290–301.

JOHNSON, ADELAIDE M.: "Sanctions for Superego Lacunae of Adolescents," *Searchlights on Delinquency* (K. R. Eissler, ed.), International Universities Press, New York, 1949, 225–245.

Juvenile Delinquency Issue, *The Child*, Vol. XVII, No. 4 (1952).

KAHN, ALFRED J.: *A Court for Children*, Columbia University Press, New York, 1953.

KARDINER, ABRAM: *The Individual and His Society*, Columbia University Press, New York, 1939.

MAHLER, MARGARET S.: "Ego Psychology Applied to Behavior Problems," *Modern Trends in Child Psychiatry* (Nolan D. C. Lewis and Bernard L. Pacella, eds.), International Universities Press, New York, 1945, 43–56.

NEW YORK CITY YOUTH BOARD: *Reaching the Unreached* (Sylvan S. Furman, ed.), New York City Youth Board, New York, 1952.

PECK, HARRIS B.: "An Application of Group Therapy to the Intake Process," *American Journal of Orthopsychiatry*, Vol. XXIII, No. 2 (1953), 338–349.

————: "Group Psychotherapy and Mental Health," *International Journal of Group Psychotherapy*, Vol. I, No. 4 (1951), 301–310.

————: "Principles and Techniques in the Integration of Psychiatric Services in a Juvenile Court with a Community Youth Program," *American Journal of Orthopsychiatry*, Vol. XXII, No. 2 (1952), 277–285.

————: "Relationship of a Court Clinic to Plans for the Mental Health Needs of Children in New York City," *Journal of Educational Sociology*, Vol. XXIV, No. 9 (1951), 544–550.

————: "Resistance in Delinquency," *Social Work in the Current Scene:* Selected Papers, 76th Annual Meeting National Conference of Social Work, 1949, Columbia University Press, New York, 1950, 378–384.

———— AND BRICK, MORRIS: "Mental Health Services in a Children's Court." To be published in the *National Probation and Parole Association Yearbook: 1953*, New York, 1954.

POLIER, JUSTINE W.: *Everyone's Children, Nobody's Child*, Chas. Scribner's Sons, New York, 1941.

"Psychodynamics of Child Delinquency: Round Table, 1952," *American Journal of Orthopsychiatry*, Vol. XXIII, No. 1 (1953), 1–69.

"The Psychopathic Delinquent Child: Round Table, 1949," *American Journal of Orthopsychiatry*, Vol. XX, No. 2 (1950), 223–265.

REDL, FRITZ: "Pre-Adolescents—What Makes Them Tick?" *Child Study*, Vol. XXI, No. 2 (1944), 44–48, 58–60.

————: "The Psychology of Gang Formation and the Treatment of Juvenile Delinquents," *The Psychoanalytic Study of the Child*, Vol. I, International Universities Press, New York, 1945, 367–377.

SCHULMAN, IRVING: "The Dynamics of Certain Reactions of Delinquents to Group Psychotherapy," *International Journal of Group Psychotherapy*, Vol. II, No. 4 (1952), 334–343.

SLAVSON, S. R.: *An Introduction to Group Therapy*, Commonwealth Fund, New York, 1943.

activities. It seemed that in his sexual activities he was the victim of more aggressive youths. In the psychiatric examination, he was quite inaccessible and unresponsive. The examiner felt that, although he showed no crystallized homosexual pattern, the boy had marked schizoid trends and that the prognosis was doubtful. There was considerable question about his suitability for psychotherapy.

At the first session of the intake group, the therapist received an entirely different impression of Leslie. He manifested considerable spontaneity, particularly in his interaction with the other boys. His affect seemed entirely appropriate and he identified readily with the experiences of some of the other group members. When one of the other boys spoke of his feelings about coming to the clinic, Leslie began to give some intimation of the attitudes that had contributed to the impression of a withdrawn person which he gave in the individual interview situation at the time of his diagnostic study.

Richard had been talking about a friend who had "spilled the beans" to the police. Leslie said, with a good deal of feeling:

> LESLIE: No, I don't want them to start asking me questions—the less questions the better.
> Richard: But the reason they try to find out things about us is so they can try to help us.
> Therapist: I wonder if you are sure that you really want things found out about you.
> LESLIE: Well, if that's your job you have to do it.

Even in this brief exchange we could see his "negativistic" feelings, which had not been expressed in the intake interview. Also we noted that he took the initiative at one point. Although all the boys had declined cigarettes proffered by the therapist at the outset of the session, Leslie some time later—when the initial tension had somewhat lessened—reached for the therapist's pack and with a casual "Do you mind?" took a cigarette and thus freed the others to follow suit.

In the second session, Leslie indicated that he was able to differentiate between the clinic and other kinds of authority with which he was familiar. One of the other boys was discussing the necessity for keeping clinic appointments.

117

John: It looks bad to the judge if the record about you is that you don't come in all the time. He will think you are not interested and it goes bad against you. You could be sent away.

LESLIE (firmly): No, you can't be sent away just because you miss an appointment, especially if you have good reason.

John: Well, the other judge said I had to come here or to the training school.

LESLIE: He can't send you away just because you would not come to clinic. You have to have a good reason for not coming though.

Leslie's responses in the group (of which we have given only a fragment) were important additions to the diagnostic information previously available. The fact that Leslie had appeared "withdrawn, isolated, and schizoid" in the individual interview still had significance, and such behavior doubtless represented one aspect of his functioning. But this type of reaction might well be a specific response to a particular kind of situation, that is, when he was confronted with an unknown authoritarian figure. Diagnostically, it is important to know that this type of response was not invariably carried over into other situations and that he was able to respond quickly under less threatening circumstances. His responses in the group indicated that his personality structure was still quite fluid and that his pathology was not so extensive as to preclude the possibility of establishing a therapeutic relationship with him. On the basis of our observations, it appeared diagnostically valid to accept Leslie for treatment and to go along with his own preference for continuing in the therapy group.

Facilitating the Decision about Future Treatment

Harry O, 14, was brought to court on a charge of unlawful entry and burglary. He displayed considerable agitation during the psychiatric examination. His personality was described as "schizoid" and he was noted to be withdrawn and apprehensive. On the basis of the material presented, he seemed unsuitable for psychotherapy. Yet, because of the heavy coercive pressures that surrounded the intake procedures in a court referral, the extent of his resistance to treatment could not be satisfactorily evaluated.

In the intake group he said nothing during the first half of the session. The therapist had asked how the fellows felt about some

118

———— (ed.): *The Practice of Group Therapy,* International Universities Press, New York, 1947.

Summary of Proceedings, Conference on Control of Juvenile Delinquency, U. S. Children's Bureau, Washington, D. C., 1952.

Szurek, Stanislaus A.: "Notes on the Genesis of Psychopathic Personality Trends," *Psychiatry,* Vol. V, No. 1 (1942), 1–6.

BIBLIOGRAPHY

————, *Statistics Division, Washington, D.C.*, 1955.

————, *Statistics Division, Some of the results of Population Censuses Proc. Pakistan, Vol. XX, I,* 1959, &c.